THE PROMISED LAND

IS VOLUME

61

OF THE

Twentieth Century Encyclopedia of Catholicism

UNDER SECTION

VI

THE WORD OF GOD

IT IS ALSO THE

137TH

VOLUME IN ORDER OF PUBLICATION

Edited by **HENRI DANIEL-ROPS** *of the Académie Française*

THE
PROMISED LAND

By *RAOUL BLANCHARD*
and M. DU BUIT, O.P.

Translated from the French by ROBERT HUNT

HAWTHORN BOOKS · PUBLISHERS · *New York*

First Edition, September, 1966

NIHIL OBSTAT

Leonellus Swain, S.T.L., L.S.S.

Censor Deputatus

IMPRIMATUR

✠ Georgius L. Craven

Episcopus Sebastopolis Vicarius Generalis

Westmonasterii, die VI OCTOBRIS MCMLXV

9575

CONTENTS

PART II

TOPOGRAPHY AND ANIMAL LIFE
by M. Du Buit, O.P.

PART III

A HOLY LAND
by M. Du Buit

P A R T I

GENERAL GEOGRAPHY

by

RAOUL BLANCHARD

CHAPTER I

PHYSICAL FEATURES

Simplicity is the general characteristic of the physical geography of the Holy Land; but it is a harsh simplicity, both of climate and surface relief.

Relief

The relief falls into four main bands which run north–south parallel to the Mediterranean seaboard. From west to east they are: the maritime plain, the ridges of Palestine and Galilee, the Jordan rift valley and the Transjordanian plateau.

The coastal plain forms a kind of narrow pavement stretching from the sea to the first mountain slopes. In the south, it broadens out to a width of about 20 miles; in the north, it narrows gradually until it is no more than about 7 miles wide. The Carmel spur juts out from the mountains in the north and cuts across the plain, but the latter continues on the other side of the spur and, still narrow, grows smaller and smaller until it meets the Lebanese border. The plain is a narrow strip of land, but a very valuable one.

It is a zone which in distant geological periods was continuously covered by the sea, and today the soil is still composed of recent marine sediment—for the most part fine sand. The latter has been packed together along the seaboard by the coastal current, and heaped up by the

westerly winds to form dunes. These are particularly pronounced south of Jaffa—they can be 3 miles in width here
and 100 ft in height. Dunes have buried the whole of the
ancient city of Askalon (Ashkelon), completely covering
its 36-ft ramparts. Fortunately, the belt of dunes narrows
towards the north and there is even an occasional break
in them. Their presence produces some advantages, but still
more disadvantages. The sand of the dunes absorbs water
rapidly and so provides reserves from which plants may
profit; but the dunes tend to invade the good land in their
rear. They also prevent the passage of rivers and streams
coming down from the interior, which then overflow and
form marshland. In places the sand sets solid into a stone
called Kurkar, which is totally untillable. And lastly, this
straight coastline edged with dunes is very unsuitable for
maritime activities.

Behind this rampart of dunes, the soil of the plain has a
top layer of red sand and constitutes some of the best land
in Palestine, at least where there are no concretions, or
Nazzaz, beneath the soil; these are hard slabs similar to the
alios (iron pan) found in the Landes of Gascony, and they
prevent the roots from penetrating any further. The
precious red sands have also frequently been buried beneath the deposits brought down by streams flowing from
the interior: fine alluvial mud full of stones. Therefore the
coastal plain suffers many drawbacks, and yet this area
is the most valuable part of the Holy Land.

Behind the coastal plain stand the mountains of Palestine and Galilee, arranged in several groups, each with a
distinctive shape and altitude.

At the extreme southern end, the folds of the Negev
(Negeb) run in a south-west to north-east direction, and
form an assembly of low ridges; there are no less than nine
anticlinal ridges (raised folds) with synclinal valleys between them. Occasionally the anticlines have been broken

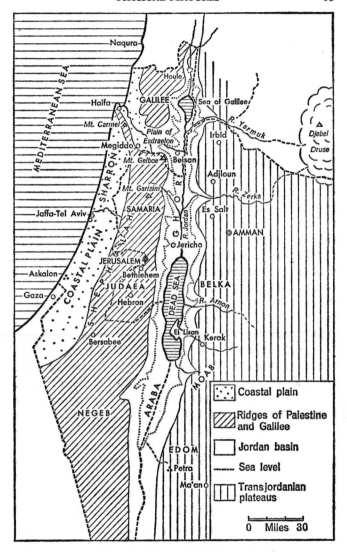

NATURAL REGIONS OF THE HOLY LAND

by erosion, formerly severe, into depressions similar to
those seen in the Bray district of the Paris Basin. The altitude does not exceed 1640 ft anywhere.[1] Going north, these
modest altitudes further decrease towards the Bersabee
depression, which is a very ancient feature of the structure
where the sea still encroached at the end of the Tertiary
period.

The true mountains of Palestine rise slowly to the north
of the Bersabee (Beersheba) depression. These are modest
mountains whose culminating point rises to only 3370 ft.
Their skeleton is made up of thick layers of hard limestone
of the middle Cretaceous period, bent into folds with a
large radius of curvature and lying in a south-south-west
to north-north-east direction. First there is the anticlinal
ridge of Hebron running as far as Bethlehem, then a central
anticlinal ridge continuing in echelon formation up to the
Gelboe (Gilboa) mountains, and finally the anticlinal ridge
of Um-el-Fahm, separated by the very low-lying synclinal
valley of Mageddo (Megiddo) from the Carmel ridge, which
is itself formed from several tight folds of the same limestone. These are only large undulations, fluctuating gently
between 2296 and 2952 ft and running from north to south
for about 90 miles. This solid mass drops away on both
sides: a very steep scarp falls away on the eastern flank,
while on the western side the ground dips gently. More
recent strata, which on the higher parts of the fold have
been removed by erosion, appear on these flanks. The
Senonian chalk which only subsists in outliers concealed
in the synclinal folds on the Palestinian axis, lines the
entire eastern slope, where it has been severely dissected by
erosion, and to the west it stretches in a continuous band
where the valleys descending from the highlands suddenly

[1] Except in the southern Negev which is today part of modern
Israel, but which was not part of the former Palestine, and where
for about 20 miles the altitude reaches 3280 ft.

widen out. Above it lies another stratum, more recent still, nummulitic limestone, which is tougher than the chalk and forms a small cliff as it meets the latter. This layer dips gently down to the littoral plain and makes an intermediate zone between mountains and plain; it is called by the Jews the Shephalah, which means the Country Below.

The mountains of Palestine which were sinking gently northwards in the north end at a fracture, a transverse fault identical to that at Bersabee (Beersheba) but more sharply defined. In the north-east the Carmel folds hit a fault running NW–SE, and the Gelbo (Gilboa) mountains also end at a fault. A wide depression extends at their base: the Plain of Esdraelon or of Jezreel, which is continued eastwards by the Beisan corridor. Through here, in the Pliocene period (end of the Tertiary), the sea found its way into the Jordan trench. The altitude remains very low here, as the watershed between the Mediterranean and the Jordan rises only to 230 ft. Thick alluvial deposits built up in this depression, mixing up together the limestone alluvium from the south and the volcanic deposits brought down from the north, and thus creating a magnificent black-earth district possessing the most fertile soil in the Holy Land.

North of the Plain of Jezreel, the mountains reappear in Galilee. They are still the harsh limestone of the Middle Cretaceous, but their type is different from that of the southern mountains. Indeed, Galilee contains the first indications of the Lebanon, but a Lebanon much disturbed by faulting. These faults run from east to west and cause Lower Galilee to fall away southwards in a series of irregular steps; Upper Galilee has the highest altitudes in Palestine (3960 ft). In addition, a flow of basalt poured down over the south-east flank, drowning the region as far as the Plain of Jezreel. All these geological accidents have occurred recently and still do; Galilee is frequently shaken

by earth tremors. Thus, Galilee, although it is more variegated and smiling than the highlands of Judaea, leads a
more hazardous existence.

East of the Palestinian mountains there occurs the most
striking feature in the relief of the Holy Land. This is the
Jordan rift valley, which stretches for some 260 miles from
north of the Houleh (Houlé) depression to the Gulf of
Akaba. Following the abrupt eastern scarp of the mountains, and dominated by an even steeper rim to the east, it is
indeed a valley of astonishing depth. The tiny Houleh basin
in the north, nestling beneath the hills of Upper Galilee, is
only 230 ft above sea level; but the level of the waters of
Lake Tiberias (or Sea of Galilee) has already dropped to
685 ft below that of the Mediterranean; moreover, the Jordan valley which continues southwards from there is lower
still, and finally the level of the Dead Sea is 1285 ft below
that of the Mediterranean, while the deepest part of the
Dead Sea is 2624 ft below the level of the coast. Going
south for another 38 miles of that part of the valley called
the Araba, the altitude remains below sea-level, and then
it slowly rises towards a low sill before dropping down
again towards the Gulf of Akaba.

This enormous gash in the earth's surface appears to
have a very long history behind it. It seems that a fold-line
followed this direction since the end of the Primary age.
In its present form, however, it is very recent, dating from
the very end of the Tertiary or the beginning of the
Quaternary; moreover the movements have not ceased,
and it is possible that the graben (rift valley) may continue
to sink and that earthquakes may shake its edges. What is
more, these edges are quite different. The western edge is
the scarp of the Palestine mountains, a scarp, it is true,
that is very precipitous, and this factor has allowed erosion
to cut severely through the weak Senonian chalk layers;
but on the eastern side a fault of enormous dimensions has

taken place, and along it the compartment of the rift valley sank while the Transjordanian plateau was pushed up to a great height, and now it looks down from 5900 ft on to the deepest part of the Dead Sea.

Finally, the different elements of this long trough have evolved differently ever since they were in position. The northern part was cut off from the rest by a flow of basalt emitted by the volcanoes of the Djebel Druze, and this formed a marshy plain containing the shallow waters of Lake Huleh (it has now been drained). After tumbling in rapids over the basalt dyke, the Jordan comes to rest in the basin that holds the pleasant, spreading waters of Lake Tiberias, which is itself blocked at the southern end by another flow of basalt. After this, there stretches southwards as far as the Dead Sea the deepest section of the rift valley called the Ghor, that is the hollow or the hole, and

GEOLOGICAL CROSS-SECTION FROM
THE MEDITERRANEAN TO THE TRANSJORDANIAN PLATEAUS

1. Quaternary and Pliocene.
2. Nummulitic limestone.
3. Senonian chalk.
4. Cretaceous limestones.
5. Petra sandstone.
6. Crystalline base.

this is about 6 miles in width. In former times it was entirely occupied by a large lake, the residue of which is now the Dead Sea. The waters of the latter contain thick layers of a saline marl deposit, called Lisan marl, after the peninsula which juts out from the eastern shore of the Dead Sea. Finally, as the level fell, the Jordan cut in the marl a valley which broadens out to a width of 7 to 10 miles as it goes south, and here we have a whole series of tight meanders. Beyond the Dead Sea, the Araba, which is completely without any watercourse, is being gradually filled with the debris falling down from the mountain-sides, especially from the lofty eastern cliff which plunges down from 4920 ft.

This cliff bears the Transjordanian plateau, the last unit in the relief of the Holy Land, and also the highest. The cliff itself is beautiful. Whereas the Judaean side of the Ghor is shapeless and full of cracks and lacerations, the wall formed by the Transjordanian edge is solid, deeply coloured and majestic. The ground was raised with such force that the deep-lying rock layers were pushed up to the surface. Indeed, if we go from the extreme south-eastern tip of the Dead Sea and follow the entire length of the Araba, we see the layers of the crystalline rock base cropping out at the bottom of the slopes. Above this layer, and rising up one above the other, are thick layers of sand-stone, known by the name of Nubian sandstone. This produces along the wall a band of bright colours ranging from red to purple and orange. Right at the top finally we find once more the grey shades with the ramparts of the Middle Cretaceous limestones, which are slightly folded like the Palestine ones, and so a spacious undulating relief is produced. Starting at the northern end, then, we have the synclinal area of Irbid, roughly between 1310 and 1640 ft, which slopes away gently towards Syria. Next there is the Adjloun dome, rising to 4068 ft, then the Salt syncline

(3181 ft), and so on until we reach the more pronounced bulges beyond the Dead Sea, which are more than 5577 ft above the Araba. Thus the plateau is not a strictly uniform tableland, but a terrain at least as varied as that of the mountains of Judaea. Moreover, in places watercourses that have been attracted downwards by the deep-lying base-level of the Ghor and the Araba, have made deep, clean-cut gorges in it. For example, there are the Yarmouk and Zerka passes in the north, the fantastic Arnon canyon which comes out at the Dead Sea; and further south the even more extraordinary gorge of Petra, where the Sik pass is such a narrow cleft that there is scarcely enough room for two camels to pass each other. Thus the Transjordanian edge has a striking appearance. These features, however, gradually become more uniform towards the east, where the slightly undulating platform falls away slowly towards the Sirhan depression in the middle of northern Arabia.

Such, then, are the main features that go to make up the fairly simple relief of the Holy Land. These moderate heights, deep depressions and plains do not look as if they would be a disadvantage to man. But there is a further factor to be reckoned with here, and that is the climate.

Climate

The Holy Land borders on the Mediterranean, but on the most southern and eastern part of it. Therefore, we must expect here a Mediterranean climate that is exaggerated, one already with a certain bias towards desert conditions. This is a general characteristic which will be varied by altitude and differences of latitude.

This country is a hot region. The average annual temperature, around 50° F at Paris, is here between 68 and 70° F along the coast, 70° on the Shephalah and 68° in the northern Negev. Temperatures are much higher than this in the rift valley: 73·4° on the shores of Lake Tiberias,

GENERAL MAP OF THE HOLY LAND

75·2° in the southern part of the Ghor near Jericho, and 77° south of the Dead Sea. Altitude, however, brings in gradations; for instance Jerusalem, situated at 2690 ft, has only 62·6°, and on the highest hills in the Palestine mountains, north and south of the city, the average can be as low as 59°, while the highest points in Upper Galilee have no more than 53·6°. Likewise, the average temperature on the Transjordanian plateau is not extreme: 64·4° at Irbid, 60·8° at both Amman and Kerak, and 55·4° even on the highest ridges in the south. But an average temperature is not very significant; it will be preferable to look at the summer and winter seasons.

The July averages are high: 78·8° to 80·6° on the coast; 79·7° on the Shephalah; 86° at Tiberias, 89·6° at Jericho; and 91·4° south of the Dead Sea. The high zones themselves are hot: 76° at Jerusalem, 69·8° on the Palestinian mountain tops, and 73·4° at Amman. However, the maxima are much higher, and this is the important fact. On the coast the average maxima rarely rise above 86°, but in the northern Negev we get temperatures of 86° and more from the end of April until mid-November. From June until September the maxima exceed 104° at the head of the Gulf of Akaba; at Amman, which lies at 2363 ft, the average maxima may rise above 86° for five months of the year, from the end of April until the beginning of October. The summer becomes unbearable when the khamsin blows. This is a dry east wind which is drawn westwards whenever low pressure remains for long over the Mediterranean. We can say quite definitely, therefore, that the summers here are very hot.

The Holy Land also experiences a winter, at least in the elevated areas, for the low-lying areas are spared it. The average January temperature varies between 55·4° and 59° along the coast; it is 53·4° on the Shephalah and the plain of Jezreel, 57·2° at Tiberias, 59° at Jericho and 60·8° south of the Dead Sea. But the northern Negev gets no more than 51·8°, Jerusalem 50° and Amman 46·4°. This does not seem so bad when it is remembered that the average in Monaco for the coldest month of the year (February) is 50°. However, account must be taken of some real cold-waves. Every winter it freezes on high ground, and the plains themselves are not immune to this danger when the east wind rages during that season. On the other hand, the Shephalah is unaffected as it is protected by the pheno-menon of temperature inversion.

This examination of temperatures is not depressing. Of course, there is a great variation: a burningly hot summer contrasted with a winter which can bring the temperatures down to below zero. This is no great disadvantage for it is better to have this kind of climate than a moist equatorial one. But one can readily appreciate that this kind of climate entails an abundant precipitation, and it is here that the root of the trouble lies. In the Mediterranean region, this precipitation (rain and snow taken together) diminishes the further we go from the Atlantic, and so it cannot be expected to be copious in the Holy Land. However, two factors, altitude and latitude, combine here to intervene and cause variations.

Accordingly, therefore, the rainfall is heavier on high ground, and heavier in the north than the south. Upper Galilee, thus, has the maximum: the highest hills receive 47·2 ins., the highest for the Holy Land. The Mount Carmel ridge, which, however, does not rise above 1804 ft, profits from its proximity to the sea and its northern situation: it receives 31·5 ins. The highlands of Judaea, higher but more southerly, do not receive any more than this, and Jerusalem only has 27·5 ins. The parts of the Transjordanian edge, which are farther away from the sea but higher than the Palestinian crests, receive 31·5 ins. at their highest points. Amman has 27·5 ins.—as much as Jerusalem. However,

towards the south the highlands overlooking the Araba on
the east, which are the highest ones in the region under
study, collect scarcely 17·7–19·7 ins.

The low-lying areas are those with the greatest deficiency.
Thanks to its proximity to the sea, the coastal plain can
just manage with its 19·7–23·6 ins. But already it is scarcely
19·7 ins. on the shores of Lake Tiberias, 11·8 north of the
Ghor, scarcely more than 3·9 at Jericho, 1·9 south of the
Dead Sea. Similarly, Beersheba hardly gets 9·8 ins. of rain,
and Eilath at the head of the Gulf of Akaba 1·9. This
means that a whole area of the Holy Land is subject to a
desert climate.

Considering these precipitation totals, it might be
thought that vast sectors are not too badly provided for,
since they exceed or equal the total for Paris, which is
23·6 ins. But it must be observed how this rainfall is distributed. Paris has some 140 days of rain per year; Upper
Galilee has only 80, the Carmel ridge 70, Jerusalem 55,
Amman 50 and the area south of the Dead Sea 10. This
shows that the Palestinian rains are quite different from
the Paris ones, and in all cases more violent. Almost every
year destructive torrential downpours occur. They may be
found as far down as the extreme southern tip of the
country, and a few years ago, it will be remembered, there
was a similar downpour which caused a flood to go rushing
through the narrow Petra pass, carrying away some tourists
who had ventured in there. There is here another difference
from the Paris rain cycle, and it is one which is even more
unfortunate: whereas at Paris it rains during all four
seasons and consequently humidity is evenly distributed
throughout the whole of the year, the precipitations in the
Holy Land are of the Mediterranean type, that is to say,
distributed over one half of the year only, leaving the other
half completely dry. The rains start in October quite
lightly, reach their maximum during the winter, from

December to March, and the last light showers fall at the beginning of May. From then until October, the Holy Land lies at the mercy of the scorching sun. Lastly, these rains, falling during one season only, are deplorably irregular from one year to the next. Let us take for instance the 1944–5 winter: Hebron received 51·2 ins., Jaffa 31·5, the Carmel ridge 43·3, Tiberias 25·6. But during the 1931–2 winter, Hebron had only 19·7 ins., Jaffa 13·6, the Carmel ridge 21·7 and Tiberias 9·8. In 1920, Jerusalem had as much as 52·6, but in 1921 only 13 ins. Consequently there is constant anxiety over the punctuality of this uncertain rainfall. If the rain is late in autumn, ploughing and sowing are endangered; if it ends too early in spring, then the harvests are threatened.

The scanty rainfall, entirely absent for part of the year, moreover, makes the sun's task all the easier. And so the sun pours down on the Holy Land. Whereas the average annual insolation at Paris is 1870 hours, and at Nice 2800 hours, the figure for Ramle on the coastal plain, where the closeness of the sea causes some fog, is 3400 hours. The figure rises to 3600 at Amman. Therefore evaporation is excessively high. In Galilee and the coastal zone already, evaporation may easily account for an annual water loss of between 3·1 and 3·5 ins. At Jerusalem this loss is 39·7 ins., at Tiberias 40·9, at Jericho 78·7, in the area south of the Dead Sea 78·5, and at Eilath on the Gulf of Akaba 81·5. From this we can conclude that atmospheric humidity is very limited. Humidity reaches 70 per cent along the coast, 70 per cent in Galilee, 65 per cent on the ridges of Judaea and the Transjordanian edge, but it sinks to 55 per cent north of the Dead Sea, 50 per cent south of it, and 40 per cent at the southern end of the Araba, which is one of the driest parts of the world.

These conditions are at least those constituting a healthy climate. To a certain extent here, Nature, despite its harshness, makes up for this lack of humidity by providing the parched ground with an abundance of dew during the hot periods; in fact the Jews of old took the absence of dew to be a sign of God's anger. Along the coast there are as many as 200 nights of dew, and even more still on the Plain of Jezreel, 130 on the Judaean ridges, and about 100 on the Transjordanian plateau. The amount of water deposited by dew has been measured and is found to be quite considerable: 3·9 ins. on the coastal plain, 4·7 in Upper Galilee and the Plain of Jezreel, 0·071 to 3·9 on the Palestine ridges, up to 5·9 near Gaza; but once again the Ghor is treated unfavourably: 1·2 near Tiberias, 0·39 at Jericho, and 0·2 around the Dead Sea. The value of the dew for plant growth cannot be overstated. Nothing could grow in the Negev in the hot season were it not for the dew.

It can be seen clearly from examining the above climatic data, that the commodity most lacking in the Holy Land is water. The proportions of this deficiency vary from north to south, from east to west and from the high ground to the low. And it is the successes and defeats in the desperate search for water that I shall point out while describing the various regions of the country.

However, before beginning this description, an observation of great importance must be made: the Holy Land today is in the middle of a period of transition, one might almost say gestation. There was very great need for it. After having been organized with loving care for thousands of years, the Holy Land finally fell, at the end of the Byzantine domination, that is, at the time of the Moslem decline, into a state of destitution which the passage of time has only served to increase. It is a country drained of its lifeblood, and it began to stir to life again at the beginning of the twentieth century. And the return to life, though it is magnificent in some sectors, is far from advanced. The "human" aspect that I shall portray is, therefore, the result not only of natural factors but also of the activity or inactivity of the inhabitants.

CHAPTER II

THE PLAINS

Only a small area of the Holy Land is composed of plains: perhaps one-tenth of the total land area. If the Jordan trench and the level stretch of the Ghor along the river are omitted, the only plains left are the one extending along the sea coast and the Esdraelon–Jezreel plain. Little though this is, it is the best that the country has to offer.

We know that the coastal plain extends below the Palestinian highlands, along the Mediterranean shore, in two unequal lengths separated by the blunt nose of the Carmel headland. North of the latter, the plain is nothing more than a thin strip $6\frac{1}{4}$ miles wide, which comes to an abrupt halt at Ras Naqura—the Lebanese border. To the south the dimensions of the plain are more spacious: the lowlands which are at first a narrow tongue of land below the Carmel ridge, open out in the Plain of Sharon to a width of 11 miles, increasing to $12\frac{1}{2}$ inland from Jaffa and 19 miles behind Gaza. The façade from Gaza to the foot of Mount Carmel is $81\frac{1}{2}$ miles long, while the little plain of St John of Acre in the north is 22.

The sea frontage of this littoral is a poor one—a low coastline perfectly straight and without any natural shelter, apart from the Carmel headland, and even this is without any indentation. The port of Haifa which has been built there is completely artificial. A complete harbour had been built by the Romans at Caesarea to serve as an outlet for the Plain of Sharon, but as soon as maintenance work on it ceased after the Arab invasion, it became silted up. The coast at Jaffa was the only spot to offer any shelter, thanks to the reefs which resulted from marine abrasion. There is shelter here for small vessels. The result of this lack of harbours has been that the Holy Land, until the present day at least, has never been a region with any maritime potential like that of neighbouring Phoenicia. The ancient Jews, in particular, were never interested in the sea, and later we shall see that they occupied the plain only late in their history.

Behind the shoreline comes the dune-belt, thick and unbroken in the south, but thin and broken north of Jaffa. This is yet another element of poor value, and even a dangerous one when the westerly winds blow the sand inland on to the fertile land. Attempts are being made today to fix these shifting sand-hills, and also a way is being sought of turning to good account a quality that the sand possesses, namely that of storing water. On these dunes that seem doomed to infertility, citrus fruits are now being successfully cultivated.

The real plain, however, lies to the rear of the dune-belt. It is not completely flat, for it contains a few small sandstone hillocks, and the wadis that come down from the highland slopes in the east have laid out over the surface some very flat detrital cones. The flatness is already one advantage, but there are many others. The soil is composed of red sands and alluvium, and is very fertile. Of course the Nazzaz deposits, which form in places beneath the sand, prevent roots from penetrating, but this difficulty can be overcome nowadays by means of deep-ploughing, which breaks up the deposits. Then, the most important quality of all, the plain possesses water. The climatic conditions themselves do not provide it with much: we have seen above that it receives 19·7 ins. from precipitation (only just) south of Jaffa, and 23·6 ins. to the north. This is in itself quite good, since evaporation here is less than in the interior of the country. But water comes down from the hills, and during the wet season the wadis descending from the east spring to life and become torrents whose water is carefully collected. There is even one perennial stream which comes down to Tel Aviv—the Wadi Auja (Yarkon), fed from the large spring of Ras el Ain at the foot of the highlands. The temporary watercourses, impeded by the dune-belt from reaching the sea, even suffer from the drawback of forming marshy land before they reach the dunes. And so the plain used to get too much water—a dangerous condition in this climate; these marshes were not drained until the twentieth century. However, the great water resources come not from these modest outside contributions, but lie buried in the substratum. At no great depth below the surface strata there is an extensive chain of subterranean reservoirs which are virtually inexhaustible, replenished by rain percolation and subterranean streams from the east. All along the plain the sound of pumping engines can be heard, extracting the water, which is then fed into irrigation channels.

The advantages possessed by the coastal plain have earned it a certain amount of prosperity; at least, we see that it was well populated and prosperous right from the earliest presence of man here: paleolithic and neolithic men have left behind traces of their occupation. In the second millennium B.C., the southern part of the plain was occupied by invaders who had come from afar. These were the Philistines, or People from the Sea, a vigorous and enterprising race who turned the plain into a country where life was easy, a country abounding in corn and herds. And so, the Philistines were more cultivated than their enemies the Jews, who were entrenched on their unsmiling hills and always ready to swoop down on the plain. It was

from the Philistines that the Hebrews learnt to use iron.
The Jews, surprisingly enough, did not enter the plain
until very late in their history: in fact not before the second
century B.C.

The plain belongs almost entirely to Israel today. Only
the Gaza strip breaks into it slightly in the south-west,
while the Arab kingdom approaches it at Tulkarm. It is
here on the plain that the Jewish immigrants are most
numerous, numbering at least 1,500,000. They first
appeared in 1878 when they established the colony of
Petah Tiqva inland behind Tel Aviv. Others settled in
the north on the Plain of Sharon, under the protection of
Edmond de Rothschild. There they found conditions poor:
there was a very large fellah population, weakened by the
malaria from the marshes which border the chain of
dunes. The fellahs worked for a few rich feudal families
(only 250 in the whole of Palestine), who owned nearly all
the tillable land, some of them possessing more than 25,000
acres. This population was wretched and not very dense:
the density being no higher than 158 to the square mile at
the beginning of the British Mandate. The reason for this
was that the plain had only been partly exploited. Hardly
any of the land other than the alluvial soils, the heaviest
of all, had been cultivated; here cereals were grown. But
the sandy soils, which were considered too light, were left
abandoned. And so these soils, the most valuable in the
plain today, were given up to natural vegetation, and oak
forests grew on them. This had already been the case in
the distant past, for both Josephus and Strabo describe the
Plain of Sharon as being forested.

The agricultural system of these fellahs was a very
simple one: dry farming with a two-yearly rotation of
crops: a crop of winter wheat or barley, a summer crop of
hard wheat, then a fallow season. There was no fertilizer
apart from whatever dung the sheep, goats and cattle left

on the fields while pasturing after the harvest. In addition, there was the produce from a few trees: olive, fig and apricot; and also some vegetables. This is the type of agriculture that the Jews of the early colonies first undertook. They grew above all else cereal crops, which represented 90 per cent of the produce of the land and hardly sufficed for their own consumption. But it was they who, on the outskirts of Jaffa, systematically set about the cultivation of citrus fruits, developed on the sandy soils. This cultivation had been started before their time, as early, indeed, as the eighteenth century; by 1920 it had spread over 7166 acres.

However, the numerous Jews who settled on the plain between 1920 and 1948 could not be satisfied with this rudimentary exploitation of resources. They had to find a way to combat the constant threat to harvests caused by the fickle climate, and discover new crops to grow, which could be sold. Therefore they replaced dry farming with a larger variety of rotation, including cereals in winter culture, other cereals in summer, grown with the aid of irrigation, also some vegetables, fruits, together with poultry-raising. Fodder was grown by means of irrigation, and as a result it was possible to keep milking-cows indoors; and the production of citrus fruit was stepped up. Fallow land was thus done away with and there was activity all the year round for the farming population. Of course, these changes were only possible if abundant restitution was made to the soil in the form of farm manure and chemical fertilizers.

It was difficult for a settler working on his own to make such progress. The Jewish immigrants soon devised a cooperative system of working aimed at producing greater agricultural efficiency. The cooperative idea was tried out in a series of forms and experiments evolving eventually into the communal type of village, the kibbutz. In this way, more efficient agricultural organization enabled a larger single area of land to be cultivated, and especially it now became possible to employ expensive machinery at a lower cost. The kibbutz represented an enormous step forward, which at once put Jewish agriculture far in advance of that of the Arabs.

But a great deal of money was required for these purposes. The introduction of irrigation, the purchase of chemical fertilizers and machinery all demanded a high level of investment. Also, the labour-force, which was called upon to provide highly skilled and increasingly specialized work, claimed higher wages. Thus the new agriculture needed larger sums of money; it had to produce crops with a high yield and high value. From producing cereals for local consumption, the farmers had now to concentrate on producing for a market where citrus fruit was the most important item. Indeed, in 1935 the acreage covered by this crop increased to 67,460. And this type of production, which is the most scientific of all, has led to the highly developed forms that are in evidence in Jewish agriculture today.

Indeed, the further advances made since independence point to the farming methods employed here on the plain as being models of scientific exploitation. Water is the supreme ruling factor, and after it the cost of labour. Therefore those crops which guarantee the highest yield per cubic foot of water and per man-hour have to be developed. Thus there has been a great expansion in cotton-growing in the south, because its cultivation is completely mechanized, and this includes picking and parasite control, the latter being carried out by spraying from the air. Sugar-beet and ground-nuts have also been introduced together with the cotton. Banana growing has been recently introduced and now accounts for nearly 5000 acres. Fodder is provided by summer cereals, cut while still green, and also by lucerne, irrigated by spraying. But the main crop is Jaffa oranges, which demands a great deal of work. It was necessary, in fact, to replant most of the orchards in order to leave enough room around the trees for the tractors to work; on the other hand, there is no longer any need to dig a hole round the trunk of each tree, in which to pour irrigation water, because the latter is nowadays distributed by aerial spraying. Of course, the growing of cereals is dwindling (except to provide fodder): it is only kept going a little in the south as a chance crop, always threatened by the uncertainty of the climate. Lastly, another ancient product, the olive, is in real decline. Here, the high cost of labour involved in maintaining the tree and gathering the fruit, all of which is done by hand, makes this crop less and less profitable to the cultivator.

For all these highly skilled types of farming, a large supply of water is needed. This is derived from the few watercourses, from springs rising at the foot of the highlands and from subterranean reserves. On average, 7148–7863 cu. ft of water per acre is used over the greater part of the plain; 7863–8578 cu. ft in the south, where it is drier. But there are crops that demand more: 11,438–14,296 cu. ft for cotton, 12,866–20,014 for lucerne, depending on the latitude and the nature of the soil. The Jewish farmer, like all peasants who make use of irrigation, uses more water than is really necessary. This constitutes such a danger that the State has been obliged to create a Water Board. A public service supplies the precious liquid, and the Board determines the quantity due to each village and sometimes even the estimated monthly supply. This goes to show the extent to which agriculture here is controlled, and this is further seen in the commercialization of the produce, again a matter for the State.

In short, agriculture on the plain has today taken on an aspect which was never seen there before: that of a varied, scientific culture of the kind that is only found in the most highly developed countries, a "western" type of agriculture transposed to a completely Semitic land. But the people living here perform many other tasks besides agriculture. Out of the million and a half local population, hardly 16 per cent is engaged in work on the land. The remainder are mostly city-dwellers employed in either public or private enterprise, in industry, building, commerce or transport. Instead of the small fortified towns, few and far between, huddled up against the coastline, for the whole length of the plain there are sizable villages and small towns, such as Ramle or Lydda (present-day Lod), and lastly a city which can be described as gigantic for this country. In actual fact, the old town of Jaffa gradually provided itself with a Jewish suburb, called Tel Aviv, further along the coast to the north. But as Jaffa spread southwards as far as the dunes, Tel Aviv spilled over eastwards towards the interior. Today new suburbs are reaching out across the plain as far as the eastern edge, and as a result we find a rather shapeless agglomeration with a population exceeding 400,000. In 1959, the density per square mile in the small district of Tel Aviv was nearly 10,000. The density remains high, however, in the rural areas: 777 in the northern, tapering part of the plain, 839 in the central portion stretching from latitude 36° to the latitude of Jerusalem, after which it starts to diminish towards the south.

These are enormous changes, and all of them have brought in their wake remarkable improvements. However, the plain has lost a major rôle that it once possessed, one which brought with it as many misfortunes as benefits: this had been to act as a great thoroughfare linking Egypt with the vast expanse of Asia. The railway-line is cut at the end of the Gaza strip, and now only rifle shots are exchanged at the frontier. Nevertheless, the plain still retains an outlet: this is the Megiddo depression, which lies in the north-east and leads to the rest of the Jewish land.

This depression forms a break in the folded mountains, cutting across between Mount Carmel and the Palestine ridges. It is not a completely flat zone: the altitude fluctuates up to 1640 ft; but it is a low-lying area when seen in the setting of surrounding heights. Irrigation is more difficult here, and the type of agriculture is different from that of the coastal strip, for here we find cereals in predominance. A curious fact, also, is that the Jewish population here is low, the majority of the cultivators being Arabs, who try more or less skilfully to imitate the agricultural methods in use along the coast. But the Megiddo depression is also the corridor which provides communication between the north of Israel and the south, and which gives access to Israel's great port of Haifa. The part played by the corridor as a means of movement is a very old one: fifteen centuries before Christ, the Egyptians were already fighting here against the peoples of the north; famous conquerors, too, passed through it: the brutal Assyrians and Nabuchodonosor (Nebuchadnezzar), then Alexander the Great, Pompey, Chosroës, Napoleon, Ibrahim and many others besides.

Megiddo gives access to another plain of Israel, the Plain of Esdraelon–Jezreel, which is very different from the coastal plain. It narrows into a neck towards Haifa, widens out in the middle and then narrows once again towards the south-east. It covers an area of 98,842 acres, an area considerably less than that of the coastal plain. But here we find the richest soil in the whole of the Holy Land: thick alluvium, to which is added limestone and basalt deposits, which have produced a rich black earth. This is able to give the best harvests of all, after preliminary drainage operations have been carried out.

Thus, this fertile terrain has been the main objective for

Jewish colonizers right from the beginning of the century. They patiently bought out the great Arab landowners and so occupied the whole plain; there is now no other part of Israel in which there are fewer Arabs to be seen than here on this favoured spot. There is a strange paradox here: when the successors of Moses occupied Palestine, the Plain of Jezreel remained for a long time in the hands of the Canaanites and was not conquered until a late date. Moreover, when the new Jewish settlers first managed to gain a foothold there, it was in a very poor state. A few corn-harvests were gathered at the end of winter, and in summer the plain was given up to the nomads from the east, who grazed their herds there.

The new settlers began here, as they did on the coastal plain, by growing cereals as a subsistence crop. This type of agriculture is, moreover, perfectly suited to the resources of the plain. Very soon, though, they saw that they could do better and produce crops for an export market. On the lighter soils on the sides of the plain they planted citrus fruit and now this area produces grape-fruit. The main portion of the plain has been largely given up to growing lucerne with the aid of much irrigation; this crop is used for cattle-rearing. The cows are kept indoors for most of the time, but they are excellent milk-producers, capable of producing annually between 989·9 and 1209·9 gallons, and some as much as 2639·7 gallons. Also, bananas are grown, but these require so much water that they are included only once in a six-year rotation, so as to prevent the land from becoming a marsh. A recent use to which the water has been put, is the creation of fish-ponds. These are artificial pools supplied by the water resulting from rainstorms. These ponds are numerous at each end of the plain and are a paying concern, for they provide the carp which are eaten on the Sabbath.

Jezreel is rich and well populated as a result of this skilful cultivation, with 518 inhabitants to the square mile. But the landscape here has remained much more rural than that of the coastal plain; it contains nothing like the conurbation of Tel Aviv, but only large villages and small towns. It is a quiet country district, possessing the most improved agriculture and lying at the foot of Mount Thabor, whose heavy limestone mass—the forerunner of the hills of Galilee—dominates the whole landscape. This mountain rises no higher than 1843 ft, yet it stands imposingly above the lowlands, and for Jews and Christians alike it is a sacred mountain.

To sum up, these plains, settled at a late period by the Jews of old and then only with caution, are today the heart of the modern State of Israel; they shelter four-fifths of the Jewish population and contain the best cultivated land and the main urban centres, with the exception of Haifa. It is here also, and particularly on the coastal plain, that Israeli industry has been set up; it includes food, textiles, non-ferrous metallurgy, cars, ready-made garments, wood, paper, glass and diamond-cutting. Fifty-two per cent of this industrial plant is concentrated at Tel Aviv. In short, the plains of the Holy Land are today a piece of the West set in the midst of the Arab world.

CHAPTER III

THE CENTRAL
HIGHLANDS

Behind the coastal plain and parallel with the seashore, there extends a ridge of highlands forming the backbone of the country. This ridge is broken by the Plain of Jezreel but reappears after the plain in Galilee. The highlands are mountains only in so far as they stand out in strong contrast to the very low areas surrounding them—the plains and the Jordan trench. In the far south, the highlands are made up of the low ridges of the Negev, after which the ground rises in height to form the broad ridges of the Judaea mountains, and then these are broken up and become the rounded tops of the Samaria hills. Finally, beyond the Jezreel plain, the hills of Lower Galilee rise in steps as far as the spurs of Upper Galilee. The maximum altitudes of these highlands are modest: 1640 ft in the Negev, 3280 ft in Judaea and Samaria and 3936 ft in Galilee. The heights are sufficient, however, to lessen the heat of summer and to produce rain a little more generously here than on the lowlands. These are superior qualities and ought to make the mountains of the Holy Land a favourite abode for man. But we shall see how, for a variety of reasons, the variation between north and south latitudes imposes less desirable conditions on the zone.

The Negev

In the far south the Negev forms a special case. Its small crests of almost inconsiderable altitude can scarcely be referred to as mountains. What counts here is the fact that they are situated in the middle of a semi-arid zone and are fringed by real desert. The annual rainfall does not exceed 7·7 ins., except in the extreme north—in the Bersabee district, and these feeble amounts get even less towards the south. At least the region possesses one real advantage: the presence in its northern sector of a thick layer of loess. This fertile soil has the valuable property of needing only a moderate amount of humidity in order to support vegetation. With the aid of the few springs, therefore, and by drawing on well-water and relying on the dew, it is possible to cultivate successfully some types of crop in this region verging on the desert.

Consequently, the Negev was populated and cultivated in ancient times, at least in its northern parts. Traces can be discovered there of settlements founded at the time of the *Pax Romana*. But since the Arab tide engulfed the Holy Land, it has reverted to a wilderness. About thirty years ago the only people to use it were the Bedouin nomads who, in the course of their wanderings, used to grow a few, hasty crops of cereals—preferably barley, as this ripens more quickly than wheat. Nothing more ambitious than this could be expected.

Everything changed when the armistice line was drawn giving Israel the whole of the northern Negev which made up more than a half of her meagre territory. Immediately, work was begun on developing irrigation by sinking wells, using pumps and laying out irrigation ditches. Jewish kibbutzim were set up and these now work with their customary fervour. Also, the Bedouin have been subjected to some discipline: they have been taught to till the land by observing the dry-farming system, with the aid of machinery. In this semi-arid climate, such a system of farming is constantly beset with uncertainties. And so the Government has instituted a form of subsidy to indemnify those cultivators working in areas which suffer from very low rainfall. The Bedouin quickly adapted themselves to the new conditions: they have almost settled down in their homes and are not slow to make use of the subsidy scheme. The subsidy has become one of the main sources of income, together with what they make from smuggling and the sale of their goats and camels for slaughter.

As yet all this is nothing more than a temporary expedient. But soon the Negev will be transformed by the results of an impressive programme which at the moment is in the process of being implemented. Fresh water, pumped from Lake Tiberias and piped across the coastal plain, is going to give moisture to these fertile lands. After that, it can be expected that all the highly productive scientific methods of agriculture, now being practised on the plains, will be introduced here on the borders of the desert, and that a numerous population will settle here. In the Negev are centred Israel's greatest hopes.

Judaea

By Judaea we mean the heavy ridges which swell up to the north of the Bersabee depression and continue until a little north of Jerusalem. They are asymmetric, dipping slowly westwards, but dropping down in abrupt scarps to the Jordan trough. And so we are led to distinguish between the low western slopes, the plateau-land of the central ridges and the precipitous eastern cliffs.

The base of the western slopes is the Shephalah of the ancient Jews—that Country Below, into which they ventured only late on, and then not without many fights, disputing ownership with the Philistines for centuries. It is the reputed scene of the exploits of Samson, whose stature

and strength speak of a man of the plains. The struggle
was worth it, for the Shephalah is a good region, enjoying
low altitude while at the same time being sufficiently above
the plain to profit from temperature inversion, which
protects it against all frost. It receives sufficient rain, and
is provided with springs at the base of the mountains. This
is the richest part of Judaea and is well suited for cereals
as well as the vine and the olive. Modern Jewish settlers
were quick to perceive these good qualities, and they
established themselves on the Shephalah early on; so
much so, in fact, that in 1948 it went to Israel, and thus
it plays a part in the rapid progress made by Israeli agriculture. Its soil, composed of alluvium transported by the
wadis, or of the products of decomposition of the limestone marls, is quite fertile and variegated; also, there is
water on the spot. Consequently, it has been possible to
mix tree crops with cereals and fodder crops, and also to
keep cattle. The Shephalah, therefore, enjoys a fair share
of the prosperity of the plain.

The scene changes as we move eastwards. Here the
slopes rise more steeply to meet the Judaean plateau,
where the altitude ranges from 2624 to 2952 ft. The nature
of the terrain alters; beyond the linear outcrop of soft chalk
which is the limit of the Shephalah, the thick, calcareous
layers of the Middle Cretaceous form from there onwards
the ossature of the ridges, and with the latter there appears
aridity, for these rocks are singularly permeable. Here,
any flowing water disappears, despite the fact that the
rainfall is heavier than on the plains. The humidity is lost
through evaporation and the porosity of the ground.
Scattered everywhere over the surface are hollows, called
dolinas by geographers; these are the result of the action
of subterranean water. There are numerous grottoes and
these have played an important part in history, for it was
in their inner recesses that the people took refuge during

the countless invasions that have swept over these regions. There are few springs and these are concealed on the valley slopes. And so cisterns are in general use here; also we find in most parts wells that have been sunk in order to get at the underground pools of shallow water lying at the bottom of the cavities. In short, Judaea is a dry region with a harsh climate; for on the one hand it is very hot there in summer, and on the other it can be very cold in winter, with the possibility of snow.

Such conditions are not very favourable to vegetation. However Judaea did at one time possess forests, but they have been destroyed since the Arab invasion and have suffered inroads from the flocks and also from men who coveted the wood for making charcoal. Today the natural vegetation amounts to nothing more than a low, thorny Mediterranean scrub, in which appear Asiatic steppe plants, including the *sidr* with its formidable hook-shaped thorns, and the thistle which is often mentioned in the Bible. A carpet of green plants springs up on the bare ridges as a result of the winter rains, but it is soon withered away by the sun in summer. The nomads completed the work of destroying the covering of vegetation; for centuries, until the beginning of the twentieth century, the Bedouin from the south and the east used to come and spend the summer on the plateaus in search of pasture.

Agriculture, therefore, is a hazardous business. The crops most extensively cultivated are cereals, a prey to the uncertainties of the rainfall, and endangered when the rain arrives too late in autumn or when the winter showers are spaced out too much or are too light. A more reliable yield is made by those plants which do not fear the parched conditions (or that fear them less): the olive, fig and vine, laid out on the terraces which edge the slopes. Flocks of sheep wander on the fallow land, while goats scale the rocky slopes. The working animals are mainly donkeys with a few pairs of oxen for pulling the swing-ploughs which turn up the *terra rossa*—the product of the decomposition of calcareous rock—at the bottom of the depressions.

The resources, thus, are meagre and only just suffice to meet the needs of the local population; there is no possibility of selling anything apart from a little olive oil and the famous dessert grapes that are grown around Hebron. There is, however, a strip of territory endowed with better natural resources: it is the corridor that climbs from the Shephalah to Jerusalem and which belongs to Israel, opening out to a width of about 12½ miles in the west and narrowing to about 6 in the east. Jewish colonists, in fact, swarmed along both sides of the railroad built in 1890 by the French to link Jaffa to the Holy City, and they have held on tenaciously to this locality in order to retain contact with the old capital. After being thus brought under energetic management, this slender neck of Israeli territory presents quite a different spectacle from the rest of Judaea. The patient Jewish cultivators have restored the thousand-year-old terraces which the former occupants had allowed to fall into disrepair. With the aid of bulldozers, they have even built new ones, which are wider in order to permit the use of machines. The latter are able to go from one terrace to another by means of ramps. The water has been carefully channelled in order to provide irrigation. The most usual type of cultivation carried out on these stretches of land, thus arranged, is fruit-growing: grapes, plums, apricots, pears and peaches. But attempts are made also to produce vegetables, to breed poultry and keep cattle. Of course fodder is not plentiful on these slopes; yet many cultivators obtain the necessary supplies for their animals from fields which they own on the coastal plain. Every morning a lorry leaves the highland village for the plain and returns in the afternoon fully loaded with fodder, lucerne or clover. This transport is an expensive arrangement, but the cost is offset by the higher prices obtained for mountain milk, the reason being that the cows of the uplands enjoy a more healthy climate than that of the plain. Nevertheless, this upland agriculture is very expensive, on account of the large amount of investment needed to prepare the terraces and also because it is burdened with the costs of transport; thus it is more expensive than that of the plain. To make good these costs, the peasants of the "mountains" have recourse to the profits to be had from tourism, taking this word in its broadest sense. During the five implacable months of summer, the air up here is more bracing and, above all, drier than the hothouse atmosphere of the plains. The people on the lowlands are only too glad to come and spend their leisure time in the hills, or to come up at the weekends. And so, in the hill villages, hotels have been built and irrigation reservoirs are used as swimming pools. The success of such enterprises has been rapid: the proceeds from tourism are now an important factor in the life of these uplands.

However this intelligent and costly new development has not been undertaken on each side of the border, which, with its barbed-wire entanglements and machine-guns, encloses the bulge of Israeli territory. Poverty is rife in the Arab part of Judaea. This is all the more terrible because in 1948 a mass of refugees left the plain and poured across the frontier into Jordan, causing there a sudden population expansion. Inside the large villages with their square, stone-built houses all huddled together, and even more so in the towns, the people are crowded into every available amount of space. In Bethlehem there are ten persons to a house, while in Hebron there are sixteen. Even these crowded conditions do not satisfy the demand for accommodation, and a large number of these unfortunate people have to find what shelter they can in tents; 28 per cent are in this predicament in Bethlehem. And lastly, others, imitating their ancestors, have taken refuge in grottoes: at Bethlehem 3 per cent live like this. The refugees live in wretched conditions, dependent upon the generosity of international organizations; for Arab agriculture, which still adheres to outdated methods, was hardly capable of growing enough to feed the normal population. And so, apart from the Israeli enclave, the Judaean plateau presents a picture of total destitution today.

As for the eastern side of the plateau which is faulted abruptly to the Dead Sea, it is no more than a wilderness— the wilderness of Juda. During the pluvial period of the Quaternary, the torrents that were attracted downwards into the well of the Dead Sea—a drop of some 3937 ft— savagely dissected this flank, which was, moreover, composed only of soft strata of Senonian chalk. This is now a mass of unstable crests, slopes of loose debris and deep ravines. This scarred mountain side is sheltered from the precipitation, which is carried by the westerly winds; and so the rains which fall on the plateau usually do not touch this side, with the result that the latter receives hardly anything more than a few winter storms. As a consequence, the population density has always been very low. At the dawn of the Christian era, it was an empty region: seekers of solitude took advantage of the fact and used to come and settle here in the grottoes. It was here that the grotto of Qumran, in which the famous Dead Sea Scrolls were discovered, lay hidden for so long. Today the wilderness of Juda is hardly used except by some semi-nomadic Bedouin. Even Israel, in spite of her bold, pioneering spirit, has not ventured to establish more than a few colonies in that southern part of it which belongs to her.

Lastly, there is a narrow band on the Judaean plateau, where man's presence has been continuous: it is the watershed between the Mediterranean and the Dead Sea—an elevated zone with views stretching away into the distance. This is the dividing line between the rolling western slopes with their occasional deep undulations and the plunging eastern scarps. It acts as a real highway—a thoroughfare linking north and south—and was formerly used by armies and merchants. Thus it is here that the towns of Judaea sprang up. To the south there is Hebron, huddling in a hollow and encircled by the highest hills on the plateau. Thirty-six thousand inhabitants are crowded into its solid, stone houses, and a few under tents and in grottoes. The reason for this is that 45 per cent of the population consists of refugees. Apart from farming, there is nothing much which offers them a living, save the minor urban crafts and a little tanning. But Hebron is also a sacred city, fired with real Moslem fanaticism, centring around the tomb of Abraham. To the north along the highway, built under the British mandate, there is Bethlehem—smaller, but enjoying much prestige as the scene of the Nativity, and accustomed to living by means of the money brought in by pilgrims. But here, too, there has been an influx of refugees, who now account for half of the population. We have seen how they have had to make use extensively of tents and grottoes. Thus there is abject poverty. A few miles further on is Jerusalem, the Holy City, which merits a separate examination.

Jerusalem

The city was originally a crossroads: the place where the north–south route along the watershed was intersected by the east–west route coming from the Jordan valley, which takes advantage of the last outlet from the valley before the obstacle of the Dead Sea. A stronghold dating back to the remote past was established here; its presence is borne out by Egyptian texts which date from before the second millennium. This is the stronghold which its occupants, Canaanites who were called by the name of Jebusites, retained for a long time during the Jewish invasion, surrendering only to David, who made it his capital. Here Solomon built the Temple, and thenceforth Jerusalem became the Holy City of the Hebrews.

This ancient city was built on a defensive position: a kind of elongated promontory with two ravines which drop away towards the Dead Sea, the Valley of Cedron and the Tyropoeon valley, and which join up below the point of the promontory. The position of this long hill was consequently very strong, since only the neck of the promontory needed to be fortified. Moreover, this spit of elevated ground, named Ophel, had an invaluable advantage: the presence of a permanent spring on the side of the Cedron valley, from which water could be diverted into the fortified enclosure. In about 720 B.C. King Ezechias made further improvements by boring a tunnel which brought the flow of water inside the ramparts from this spring of Gihon, which up till then had flowed along an open conduit. As a result, the population, when under siege, could be sure of a supply of water, while the besiegers were dying of thirst. This did not prevent the city from being besieged about ten times and from being destroyed sixteen times. However, the city has always risen up again afterwards.

Gradually, however, it has moved away from its original site. Solomon had already built the Temple outside David's city, which was restricted to the promontory. Then suburbs were built to the north and the west, beyond the Tyropoeon valley with its litter of debris. The Ophel promontory lost its population little by little, while a fresh line of fortifications was being constructed to protect the new districts. It was along this line of fortification that the palace of Herod was built, and also the Tower Antonia, where it is thought Pilate had his headquarters. The city of the Crusaders, which was later taken by the Turks, occupied the same site, and the present, picturesque fortified enclosure, with its towers and crenellations, dates from the time of Suleiman the Magnificent. Its ramparts look down on the old site of the city of David, which has become waste land. But once more the city overspilled its boundaries, reaching out northwards and particularly westwards to create fresh suburbs. Jerusalem is therefore a disjointed city, and this has, moreover, been increased by the events of 1948.

In fact there are two Jerusalems now separated from each other by a frontier as menacing as can be imagined. To the east stands the old Jerusalem, that is, the city of Herod, slightly enlarged in its Turkish enclosure; inside this enclosure are grouped together stone houses, often with a domed roof, packed together along narrow streets which are supported by flying buttresses. Seen from above, it is an uneven expanse of grey, out of which the dark finger of a cypress rises here and there. In the north-west corner can be seen the heavy mass of the Holy Sepulchre Church, rising up over the surrounding houses. But the sight that without doubt produces the most striking impression of all is the platform of the former Temple, which stands out firmly above the Wailing Wall. In the centre of this great open space, levelled by Herod, stands the pleasing dome of the Mosque of Omar, while on its south-west side is the Mosque of El Aksa—a former Christian basilica, taken over once again by Islam, who built it in the first place. Old Jerusalem is both picturesque and moving, though it is difficult to say whether this emotion comes from the appearance of the Holy City or from the strong memories attached to it.

This old city of Jerusalem, however, which is today an Arab town belonging to the Kingdom of Jordan, has become a city in distress. Out of the 50,000 or so habitants that it contains, more than a third are refugees. And so people have been obliged to crowd together: the city has an average of nineteen persons to a house, and in addition some camp out in grottoes or in tents. There is not enough work to be had, as there is hardly any industry: a dairy that is poorly supplied, and a small soap-works. But the main occupations are embroidery, wood-carving in which olive wood is used, and jewellery-making; the articles produced being intended for sale to pilgrims. For it is the tourists who come here for religious reasons that provide the main business. They consist of a few Moslems, who perform their devotions in front of the Mosque of Omar, but mainly Christians who are visiting the holy places. Now, all the holy places are situated within the Arab sector of the city: the Holy Sepulchre, the Via Dolorosa, the house of Caiaphas, and, on the outskirts of Gethsemani, the Mount of Olives, and also Bethlehem. Thus the poverty-stricken Arab town has hardly anything to live on apart from what is brought in by the Christians.

A completely different picture is presented by the Israeli Jerusalem, which lies to the west of the Turkish ramparts, on territory which the Jews secured in order to have access to the Holy City. It is like a huge suburb without any firm shape at first; out of it they have made their capital. Everything here is brand-new: the houses and public buildings contrast with the old-fashioned appearance of the old city. This yellow town is well off and full of movement: it has its administrative departments; there is commerce and even industry, such as the large shoe-factory set up by an American firm. With its wide, well-constructed streets, its modern houses and its trees, this city of 150,000 inhabitants is the complete opposite of the old, walled city. The only thing missing is the picturesqueness and also the memories.

Samaria

Going north from Jerusalem, beyond Bethel and towards Galgala and Silo, the rugged features of Judaea give way gradually to the more pleasant landscape of Samaria. The relief is responsible for this transformation: the terrain falls away gradually northwards and becomes more broken, retaining in the hollows of its folds less tough layers than the harsh Cretaceous limestone. There is even a little sunken corridor in the north-east, which prepares us in advance for the Plain of Jezreel, and along which flows the wadi Fara with a free outlet into the Ghor. There are basalt outcrops here and there right up in the north. Thus, features that belong to northern Palestine little by little begin to show. This more varied relief is also more open, and contains wide basins, broadening valleys and rounded hillocks—a landscape which contrasts with the deep gorges and steep plateaus of Judaea. In addition, the rainfall tends to increase the further north one goes, thus reducing aridity. Consequently, Samaria is a less severe region than Judaea.

Less severe means less strict in observances, and we see that, whereas the kingdom of Juda remained faithful to Yahweh, Samaria, with easier contact with the outside world, drifted more easily into the worship of false gods. The golden calf was more readily accepted there, perhaps because the region was richer. On its richer soil there was a higher yield from cereals, the vine and the olive. Backed by this seeming affluence, these northern Jews disputed political and religious leadership with Judaea. At Sichem (Shechem) at the foot of Mount Garizim (2889 ft), was the tomb in which Joseph was buried when he returned from Egypt; and also there is the well which is spoken of in the Gospel. Samaria, then, being more open, richer and more heavily populated than Judaea, quite naturally opposed the latter.

Like all the rest of Palestine, Samaria had been gradually ruined under the various rulers who succeeded each other after the Arab conquest: it was given up to the nomads from the east during the summer. The British during their Mandate made an honest effort to better conditions, by cleansing the towns, opening up a highway along the line of the highland ridge running down the whole length of the region from the Plain of Jezreel to Jerusalem, and by building a railway line from the Plain of Jezreel to Nablus, with a branch-line to the coastal plain. But here too the events of 1948 produced a state of utter confusion. The population suddenly swelled by a half through the influx of refugees. The towns and villages are filled: at Nablus (43,000 inhabitants) the newcomers make up 37 per cent of the total; at Jenin there are on average nine persons to a house, at Ramallah ten, and at Nablus fourteen. In addition, tents are used: 38 per cent of the refugees are thus accommodated at Ramallah, 15 per cent at Jenin, and 13 per cent at Nablus.

Although it is better off than Judaea, Samaria has not got a lot to offer these guests. The crops grown here are the ones typical of traditional Arab agriculture, that is cereals on a dry-farming basis, with a poor yield. The olive and the vine are more productive, but these crops are insufficient to feed, in addition to the local inhabitants, the 150,000 who have descended like a cloud of locusts on the district. And industry for its part shows only meagre resources, on account of the lack of raw materials, fuel and export markets. At Nablus, soap is produced from olive oil; indeed a factory where the oil is purified has been set up between Ramallah and Nablus. Also there is a host of craftsmen to be seen in the towns and large villages. All this, however, does not amount to very much, and Samaria is in a state of absolute poverty, just like the Arab part of Judaea. In order to find a prosperous region it is necessary once more to go to an Israeli district, this time one that lies further north.

Carmel

We have seen that the Carmel headland, the only promontory on the coast, continues the folds of Samaria on the other side of the Megiddo dip. But it fulfils quite a different rôle. Although it is much less wide and not very high (1790 ft), it is far more imposing than Mounts Garizim and Ebal in Samaria, which reach 2889 and 3083 ft, because a strongly marked fault causes it to rise up in an abrupt wall above the end of the Plain of Jezreel. As it faces the moisture-bearing west winds, moreover, it receives a rainfall which, in the Holy Land, can be called abundant; as a result it bears a more luxuriant covering of vegetation than that on the neighbouring plains. The ridge has always kept its trees, for example. Because of these features, Carmel was a place that produced feelings of wonderment and respect in the minds of the local people: a sacred mountain, filled with memories of prophets such as Elias and Eliseus, who visited the mountain frequently.

Mount Carmel is still a holy mountain, with monasteries perched on its sides commanding magnificent views over the plains and Galilee. Today, however, its major rôle lies in providing shelter from the westerly winds and heavy swells for the great sea-port of Haifa, the real outlet of Israel. The port's prosperity dates from the British Mandate, when a poor harbour was transformed into a trading port capable of handling large ships, which has since been further improved by the Israelis. The English also were responsible for making Haifa the outlet for an oil pipeline coming from Arabia, and for fitting out an oil refinery that was able to deal with 4 million tons per year. The events of 1948 put the pipeline out of operation, and the refinery is now run with oil imported from the Caribbean, since Israel is not permitted to use the Suez Canal. But Haifa has secured for herself other industrial resources. There is a large-scale cement manufacturing industry which makes use of the limestone in the mountains. There is a fertilizer and chemical-products company producing in two factories superphosphates and nitrate fertilizers. The Kaiser-Fraser establishment assembles cars; a large factory turns out tubes; and there are shipyards for new construction and repair-work. And so Haifa has become not only a busy port, but also an industrial metropolis, the main one in Israel as far as heavy industry is concerned, whereas Tel Aviv predominates in the field of light manufacturing.

The town has grown a great deal as a result of this, and today the population is coming up to 200,000. The old town, lying alongside the port, is overflowing and spreading out into new districts in every direction, while on the undulating terrain above it there is the Hadar, the commercial district. Stretching westwards as far as Cape Carmel lies a middle-class residential suburb, and above that there are villas going up the mountain-side. The outskirts are no less densely populated: the District of Haifa, which includes with the city the mountain and the edges of the surrounding plain, carries a population density of 1090 per square mile. Jews make up by far the biggest part of the population: there are barely 25,000 non-Jews, among which Christians number 10,000 and Druses 10,000. Haifa and Carmel constitute one of the main bastions of the Israeli stronghold.

Galilee

Just as the Carmel ridge was more pleasant than the mountains of the south, so also Galilee appears more smiling to anyone coming from Samaria and especially from Judaea. Going north the Holy Land becomes less rugged and austere. The contours are more varied: in the south hills encircling small basins, then small plateaus rising in steps with each fault, and finally in the north a real massif which reaches more than 3936 ft. Latitude and altitude combine to procure for the region a more abundant rainfall than anywhere else, for it is here that we have the maximum precipitation for the whole of Palestine. Vegetation is richer, therefore, in Galilee and has put up stronger resistance to despoliation than in the south. The higher zones have retained a few forests, consisting mainly of small oaks, terebinths and Aleppo pines. The land is greener: there are plenty of copious springs, and the streams are often permanent ones. This green countryside with its running waters and fertile soil—a product of basalt and limestone decay—resembles a paradise when compared with the rest of the Holy Land.

It has other unique characteristics of a more human kind. Because it enjoys easy access to the sea, to the Plain of Jezreel and the Tiberias basin, and even to the north-east via the upper valley of the Jordan, Galilee was once a meeting place, unlike Judaea with its high, isolated plateaus. Thus, disputes have always arisen over ownership; it has been a cross-roads for peoples, and, consequently, a land of Gentiles. After the Assyrian invasions, it was infiltrated by large numbers of Aramaean settlers; Hellenism left a deeper imprint here than anywhere else in Palestine; a new Jewish colonization was begun under the Maccabees; later, the Crusaders built many castles in the region and their number was added to by the feudal Mohammedans, who wanted to safeguard their passes. The Jewish colonists arrived to find a large, mixed population —one that was much less resigned to uprooting itself than other Palestinian Arabs elsewhere. In the modern Jewish State, Galilee is the province which shows the biggest proportion of non-Jews. Although eastern Galilee and the coastal area are solidly filled with Jews, the various central districts contain more non-Jews than Jews. The former are divided into different religions and sects: Christians predominating in the south, Moslems in the central areas. Among the Moslems themselves, there is a majority of Shi'a and Druses in the north. The non-Jews of Galilee have better relations with the State of Israel, it seems, than the other Arabs who remained on the territory of the Republic. The Druses, in particular, have apparently come round completely to accepting the Jewish State and seem to be serving her interests intelligently. The population is dense for a country so hilly. The figure for the whole of Galilee is 259 persons to the square mile—a very high one for a mountainous region. Unlike the rest of Palestine, where the population conglomerates in large villages around a spring or well, Galilee has its population more spread out. In Roman times the region was described as a "sea of dwellings". Nowadays, small hamlets scattered about the countryside are the rule. Towns are few in number and small in size, with the result that Galilee has remained rural in an Israel which shows such advanced urbanization (77 per cent of the population is urban). Nazareth in the south is nothing more than a large, straggling village, mostly Christian in population, sprawling on the sides of a hill. Safad, alone, has the appearance of a town, perched proudly on top of a small hill to the east and encircled with ramparts.

As a farming province Galilee is variously endowed. Calcareous platforms—real limestone plateaus—are to be found, and here goat and sheep grazing is the only use to which the land can be put. But the depressions, with their covering of soil—*terra rossa* derived from limestone and brown earth from basalt—are eminently suited to agriculture. Here the Arab element has not hesitated in following the example set by the Jews, and are pursuing an up-to-date pattern of farming. Arab peasants have organized themselves into cooperatives and have adopted mechanized methods. Although cereals are still grown for food, cash-crops are to be seen more and more in the fields. For the most part these are vegetables and fruit; their great advantage is that they ripen at the end of autumn and can therefore be marketed just when the other producers have exhausted their stocks. The Arab farmer in Galilee also carries on an unusual speciality—tobacco-growing on the fertile soil derived from basalt; and for this delicate work, which is entirely done by hand, he employs a large labour-force.

Finally, the Galilean farmers have no hesitation in going to the low areas surrounding the hills to look for resources. The Jews of eastern Galilee have acquired land in the Houleh basin, which is especially fertile and well watered. They have also introduced fish-ponds, and from them they obtain carp. There is one village, situated at 754 ft above Lake Tiberias, which has gradually come to cultivate solely the land it possesses in the depression, with the result that the actual village itself has become merely a pleasant retreat, to which the people come in the evening in order to enjoy the cooler air of the hills after the scorching heat of the lowlands. Of course, the cool air in the hills is a help in developing the tourist industry, and Galilee competes on a modest scale with Mount Lebanon in this field.

Thus, we see that Galilee has more than one claim to a position of uniqueness. It is the most pleasant region in the Holy Land; it is at present developing a sensible kind of mountain agriculture; and lastly it is the place where there seems to be some harmony growing up between the Jewish colonists and the older inhabitants, and in this there lies a real hope for the future.

CHAPTER IV

THE JORDAN RIFT

No less unique is the enormous rift that scores the Holy Land for more than 250 miles of its length. A very striking feature about the rift is its great depth, for at its lowest point it reaches some 2600 ft below the level of the Mediterranean. And so it presents a great obstacle to communications between the west and east. But it possesses another outstanding feature and that is its dryness. In a semi-arid climate such as this, a depression of these dimensions, boxed in on either side, with hardly a chance of receiving precipitation can be nothing but a kind of desert.

But as the trench extends from the north to the south and varies in depth from latitude to latitude, its desert-type characteristics also vary. They are moderate in the north, becoming more strongly marked in the south. Several different sub-regions may be distinguished in this long rift, and so we shall consider each of these in turn: first the north, comprising the Houleh and Tiberias basins; then the centre portion—the largest section of all—comprising the Jordan valley proper and the Dead Sea; and lastly the south, which is simply the Araba.

Houleh and Tiberias

The north is the most fortunate part of the rift, or rather the least unfortunate one. It is shallower and less arid than the other sections, thanks to its more northerly situation; and above all it is better supplied with running water. Moreover, it now belongs to Israel so that some prosperity may be expected for it.

The Houleh basin is a well-marked trough, a long rectangle lying between the calcareous ridges that continue the hills of eastern Galilee into Lebanese territory, and the heavy masses of basalt which originally came from the Djebel Druse. It is very low-lying, since its altitude drops to 229 ft, and on the western side it is dominated by a 2889-ft hill, while on the eastern the basalt formations rise sharply to 3280 ft. These barriers form screens, shutting out the precipitation, which amounts to less than 19·6 ins. The basin is fortunately situated close to a real mountain, one of the highest in Syria, Mount Hermon; its towering peak rises to 7546 ft and as a result receives plenty of moisture, being snow-covered all through the winter. Mount Hermon, which stands out from all other parts of the Holy Land, was once venerated as a holy mountain. But no people had ever more reason to turn their prayers towards it than the inhabitants of the Houleh depression, for it is Mount Hermon that feeds their basin with its waters. Large springs, rising on the south-west slopes of the mountain, supply the streams which come together to form the Jordan. These waters are even too abundant to get away easily, for beyond the basalt flow, which forms a sill blocking the lower end of the basin, the land has been built up and now offers no more than a slight slope. And so the waters were held back and formed marshland, while at the southern end of the basin they formed a small, shallow lake, overgrown with papyrus—the "Waters of Merom" of the ancient people, and later called the lake of El Houleh. Over the alluvium, incongruous though it may seem for Palestine, the marshes deposited a layer of peat.

Consequently, the basin was virtually a pestilence-ridden marsh when the Jewish settlers first began to develop it in the first quarter of this century. The exit passage was deepened, thus lowering the water level. The course of the river was straightened and the marshes drained. Today there are no longer any marshes, and the lake, too, has disappeared. The whole of the depression has thus been made available for cultivation. The peat has been incorporated with the alluvium by means of deep ploughing, so that a very fertile soil, with plenty of moisture, has been produced. All kinds of crops are grown here, especially fodder. Also, excellent fish-ponds have been laid out. It is one of the most rural parts of Israel with no towns, but strong settlements, guarding this strip (15½ miles long by 6) which lies between Lebanese and Syrian territory. There are only Jews in this outpost in enemy country; for when the immigrants came and settled here it was empty and so there are no Arabs there today, and for this reason it is all the better defended.

At the outlet from the basin the Jordan is fully formed. The river reaches its maximum flow during the rainy winter season (1765·7 cu. ft in February). The flow is kept up in spring because of the snow melting on Mount Hermon, and it still amounts to 176·5 cu. ft at the end of the dry season. What was a sluggish river in the Houleh basin is suddenly transformed into a kind of torrent as it flows over the basalt sill where it encounters a drop of more than 656 ft within a distance of 10½ miles. This gorge brings the river into a new bowl which is almost as long as (13 miles), and a little wider (7½ miles) than, the previous one. This bowl, too, is blocked at the far end by a flow of basalt and so the fine lake of Tiberias is formed; it is about 164 ft deep and lies 685 ft below sea-level.

This charming expanse of water with its blue waves, set
in pleasantly moulded hills, is a delightful sight in a
country where the climate is implacably hot. Men have
always taken a delight in this lake: they have also been
attracted to it from other parts by its great advantages.
For although the summer temperatures are stifling and the
rainfall is poor, yet water is readily available—virtually
in unlimited quantity—and it can be put to many uses.
First, there is fishing: a certain fisherman of Lake Gene-
sareth has become a key-figure in the world. Next there is
irrigation: in ancient times the shores of the lake were ad-
mirably cultivated and inhabited. We are told that Magdala,
Capharnaum and Bethsaida had 50,000 inhabitants at the
start of the Christian era. Josephus describes the shores of
the lake as being shaded by palms, walnut-trees, fig-trees
and olives. But when I visited these same shores in 1925
they were almost uninhabited; the denuded slopes above the
blue water showed only buffs and yellows.

Since that time, however, things have changed radically
with the influx of Jewish immigrants. The latter took possession of almost the entire periphery of the lake, except
for a few miles in the north-east, where the Syrians
retained control. The immigrants first of all planted
mimosas and eucalyptus, in order to provide shade for their
wheat and cotton fields. Later they sowed plantations of
grapefruit on the heavy soils derived from basalt. More
recently, they have come to recognize the great potential
in terms of early vegetable production which they have as
a result of the high temperatures along the shores of the
lake. Tomatoes grown here are ripe and can be marketed
four to six weeks before their normal season. And so
tomatoes were planted on the lower stretches of the banks,
and water was pumped up to them by means of small
diesel engines. These methods proved so successful that
gradually this system of watering has crept up the hill-

sides. Fields of tomatoes are now to be seen as high as 590 ft above the lake on the south-west shores, and even at 721 ft in the extreme northern end. The reason is that profits to be had are considerable, since the produce can be sold at prices eight times higher than those obtainable during the normal period of production. Consequently, poverty has made way for prosperity both on the shores of the lake and on the surrounding hills, even as far as the Horns of Hattin which witnessed the defeat of the Crusader kingdom of Jerusalem. The district is inhabited by Jews only, who are always ready to defend it, for the lake is a troubled frontier, continually harassed by the Syrians from the north-east shore.

At the southern end of the lake, Israeli territory continues for a few more miles, over the entire width of the depression, as far as the confluence of the Jordan with its tributary, the Yarmuk. There, close to the colony of Dagania, a recent discovery has shown that the Holy Land was inhabited by man right from the earliest ages. Indeed, in a stratum that has been incontestably dated as belonging to the Villafrancan period, that is a period intermediary between the end of the Tertiary and the Quaternary, bones and roughly shaped flint implements have been discovered. These are the exact replica of the "Pebble culture" found elsewhere in Africa, and which is attributed to hominoids living here before the appearance of *Homo sapiens*. Thus, man's predecessors already lived in the Holy Land—another reason for regarding it as sacred.

The Ghor

Below Lake Tiberias, and stretching for 68 miles, is the valley of the Jordan, ending at the Dead Sea. This valley is usually called the Ghor. It broadens out gradually as we go south: 4 to 5 miles in the north, and $15\frac{1}{2}$ at the level of Jericho. This long depression is entirely below sea-level,

—951 ft at the end of Lake Tiberias, and 1296 ft at the
top end of the Dead Sea. This imparts a desert climate,
with summers that are torrid and extremely dry, and a
scanty rainfall in winter. These conditions increase in
severity from north to south.

The depression was completely filled by a large lake in
the wet periods of the Quaternary. We know that thick
layers of marl, called Lisan marl, were deposited in the
lake. Since these were formed in an expanse of water of
high salinity, they are themselves impregnated with salt.
As the level of the waters fell, the Jordan cut down through
the clay, following the haphazard fluctuations of the
receding waters of the lake and tracing out the terraces,
which today are seen rising above each other in the present
valley. It is these terraces that the inhabitants call expressly
the Ghor, while they reserve the name Zor for the lower
part of the valley where the Jordan forms its meanders.

The terraces, whose marl soils are made up of calcareous and basalt debris, would be fertile but for their
salt content. In order to be cultivated, they have first to
be thoroughly flushed—a difficult operation to carry out,
as the river flows far below them. They can be cultivated
only where recent alluvial deposits coming down from
the side walls give them a covering. This is what has
happened on the right bank at the outlet of the Beisan
depression at the end of the Plain of Jezreel, and later at
the outlet of the Wadi Fara coming down from Samaria,
and also in the vicinity of Jericho. The same is true, on the
left bank, at the lower end of the Yarmuk valley and
the Wadi Zerka. In these places, the soil is free from salt
and there is water at hand, either in the tributary rivers,
or in the large springs rising at the base of the side walls,
such as the Ain-es-Sultan and Ain-Duk at Jericho. These
are, to be precise, oases, since nothing will grow outside
their favoured vicinity. They were used at a very early

date during the wet periods of the Quaternary. Excavations carried out at Jericho have revealed the remains of a town, whose date has definitely been established as 4000 B.C.; this makes it the oldest town in the world. In ancient times, all these districts were occupied, as is shown by the numerous "tells" scattered over the Ghor terraces as well as the ruins of Phaselis, Scythopolis (Bethsan) and ancient Jericho. Yet when I visited these parts forty years ago, I only met a few Bedouin there, half sedentary, engaged in a poor system of farming during the winter.

Today there is much more life on the terraces, but conditions vary a great deal. In the north Israel has secured for herself the right bank of the Jordan, and there, going south from Lake Tiberias for about 18 miles, we find that the alluvial deposits and waters of the Nahr-el-Jalud, coming down from the Beisan corridor, have been put to use with great energy. The same types of crop as on the Plain of Jezreel are seen here, as well as the fish-ponds. In the south, in Jordanian territory, the desert still holds sway over vast areas, while the few oases swarm with the great numbers of refugees. In 1925, Jericho had been a wretched cluster of huts, huddled together around a spring that supplied water for some date-palms and a few orange-trees. Today, however, Jericho's population numbers 45,000, of whom more than 80 per cent are refugees; some of them crowd into the small oasis dwellings and others into tents or huts, profiting from the fact that inclement weather is a rare occurrence here; these refugees scarcely improve conditions in the oasis by their presence.

The terraces plunge down into the valley, the Zor, whose soft sides are often deeply incised by violent erosion, produced by the infrequent but very heavy rainstorms. And so the hillsides have been eroded into a forbidding, bad-land landscape. The river receiving the silt thus washed down is muddy, and its salinity, which is already felt as it leaves Lake Tiberias, is further increased by the addition of this salt-charged alluvial clay. It is not an insignificant water-course. In an average year it yields 19,069,992,000 cu. ft of water at the outlet of Lake Tiberias; and a few miles further on it receives almost the same amount from its tributary, the Yarmuk (16,951,104,000 cu. ft). Of course all along it suffers losses from evaporation. But it is replenished from both sides of the valley, in particular from the Wadi Zerka. From the Transjordanian side alone, the volume of water that is added to the Jordan can amount to 2,825,184,000 cu. ft per year. And so the river succeeds in reaching the Dead Sea, even at the end of the summer season.

The valley is used very little. In 1932, during the British Mandate, a power station was built at the confluence of the Yarmuk and the Jordan; and this made use of the combined waters of the two rivers. Beyond this point, however, the gradient of the river-bed is reduced, and the river begins to meander crazily, with the result that its length is greatly increased. Over a distance of about 62 miles as the crow flies, the Jordan manages to achieve a length of 199 miles. In this desert, the presence of a ribbon of water has given rise to the appearance of virtually a tropical vegetation—a thick jungle, infested at one time by large wild animals. Seen from the air, this dark band of vegetation, clearly defining the loops made by the river, shows up in striking contrast with the greys and whites of the almost bare wilderness on either side. Yet there are no human beings to be found along these banks. The valley becomes inhabited only at its lower end where the Jerusalem–Amman road crosses the river by the Allenby bridge, quite close to the spot where the Hebrews crossed the Jordan to go with Josue to lay siege to Jericho.

The Dead Sea

The Jordan empties into a sizeable lake, as long as Lake Geneva (47 miles) and 10 miles wide at its widest part. This is what is left from the waters which occupied the entire area of this huge depression in former times. Evaporation, as we know, is very great here. However, apart from the flow it receives from the Jordan, the lake obtains quite considerable amounts from the rivers and streams coming down from the plateaus of Transjordan, the biggest of which is the Arnon whose annual yield amounts to 2,118,888,000 cu. ft. The Judaean slopes contribute to the supply with their temporary wadis and also their springs, some of which are hot and occasionally saline. And so the water level is maintained, though with slight fluctuations: in 1885 it was 1295 ft below the Mediterranean, in 1915 it had risen to 1269 ft and in 1941 it had once again fallen to 1298 ft. In addition, the level rises slightly at the end of the winters, the annual variation being from 15 to 19 ins.

But whether it is lower or higher, the Dead Sea is constantly being enriched with salts; this is a result of evaporation and the reception of saline spring-water. Magnesium chlorides are the main constituent of this salt concentration, but there are others strongly represented too: sodium chloride, calcium chloride, potassium chloride, bromides, sulphates and carbonates. At the surface, the concentration of salts reaches 21 per cent—an extraordinarily high percentage. I tasted a little Dead Sea water near the place where the Jordan enters and I found it most unpleasant. It is much worse at a depth of about 65 feet, and also on the eastern and western shores where the water is not changed. In such places the water is practically saturated. This explains why there is no life in this lake or on its banks. The Dead Sea certainly earns its name.

However, there are several centres of human activity on the sides of the lake: at the foot of the mountainous sides there are two oases, while at the ends there are real industries.

The eastern shore is closely overlooked by an imposing, straight wall of rock. This is the platform of the Trans-jordanian plateau, split here and there only by abysmal canyons. But two-thirds of the way along the shore, going south, projecting from the foot of the rift is a peninsula, shaped like an irregular rectangle; it is made up of the marls that were deposited by the great lake of the Ghor in the Quaternary. This is the El Lisan peninsula, which separates the lower, shallower end of the Dead Sea from the rest. At the start of the peninsula, there is the small settlement of El Mezre, fed by water coming down from the cliff, and also a sparse pasture frequented by the Bedouin. The western side, though less elevated, is more tragic in appearance, with the surface of its hills ripped open by ravines and fringed by detritus-falls; there is not a scrap of vegetation to be seen. The ruins of the stronghold of Masada, the last refuge of the Zealots from Titus, is a fitting accompaniment to this dead landscape. However, halfway between the two ends of the Sea, a detrital cone has developed a small alluvial strip above the water. This is the site of the oasis of Engeddi. Now Engeddi has re-mained in the possession of Israel, an outpost beyond the Jordanian bulge of Hebron. Jewish initiative has made remarkable use of this exposed territory. Taking advantage of the temperature, which from the end of winter, and even in winter, is very high, the settlers have engaged in the production of out-of-season vegetables and fruit. Thus, as early as the end of January they put on the market excellent tomatoes, and also table grapes; and between December and April they grow fine roses, which are un-equalled on the market. Engeddi's prosperity is a challenge to the atmosphere of death that hangs over the surrounding area.

In addition, an industry has sprung up at the only two places where access might be gained to the sea without too much difficulty: namely, the lower Jordan plain in the north, and in the south the sebka (salt marsh) where the Araba begins. In these places it was possible to exploit the wealth of the Dead Sea, that is, its enormous concentration of salts. It is estimated that it contains 1,968,420,000 tons of potash, and 885,789,000 tons of magnesium bromide. The extraction process consists in the water being pumped up through pipes that are lowered to a great depth, where the water is more heavily charged with salts than at the surface. Then the water is allowed to evaporate in the sun, after which there only remains the task of flushing away the impurities. In 1930, an English company, the Palestine Potash Company, set up two factories: one in the north at Kallia, and the other in the south at Sodom, which takes its name from the damned city of Sodom whose site is probably somewhere in these parts. The company did considerable work, especially during the war, when the production of potassium chloride exceeded 98,421 tons; and this covered half the United Kingdom's needs. In addition, the company produced salt, carnallite, bromine, bromides and magnesium. The Kallia factory was destroyed in 1948 at the time of the fighting, but was re-opened by the Jordanians in 1952, and once again it produces potassium and magnesium, which, however, are difficult to transport, since all ways to the west are closed. Sodom, lying in Israeli territory, operates under Government control, and a road has been opened up across the mountain-side to link with Bersabee. This factory is of vital importance in supplying part of the huge quantities of fertilizers required by the Israeli agriculture. Consequently, through the products that are obtained from it, this formidable Dead Sea has become a source of life.

The Araba

The same is not true, however, of the Araba, for indeed it seems that there is nothing that one can hope to gain from this region.

It is a long depression, as we know, a few miles in width, stretching for about 93 miles from the Dead Sea down to the Gulf of Akaba, roughly in a straight line, shut in continuously between two steep slopes, of which the eastern one is the higher and the more abrupt. Although it is very sunken below sea-level in the vicinity of the Dead Sea, the trench gradually rises to the south before falling again slowly towards the Gulf. In any case, for its whole length it is a very low-lying channel, which remains deeply boxed-in, as though it were protected.

In this southern latitude we are in a truly arid climate: the Araba valley is especially poorly endowed with moisture. The average annual precipitation is, as has been stated before, the lowest for the Holy Land: 1·97 ins., distributed very irregularly. Also evaporation reaches its maximum here. The Araba is a real desert, therefore, without any kind of vegetation, an avenue given up to the mineral kingdom. It is choked with alluvial sand and detritus that have come down from the walls, it is completely uninhabited. Moreover, the Araba marks the political border between Israel and Jordan, an added misfortune, since as a result of this the valley is no longer a safe place in which to venture. It seems to be under a curse, for the establishment of the frontier put a stop to the flow of trade carried on by the caravans which came from Petra to the west, and which used to cross the Araba after they had gone round the obstacle of the Dead Sea.

Apart from Bedouin, who slip across the border clandestinely, no people live here, and the only permanent settlements are in the extreme southern tip of the valley, where it meets the Gulf of Akaba, and where the rift continues under the sea, getting deeper as it goes. At the point where the Gulf joins the Red Sea, the depth is already more than 9186 feet. The Jews have made sure of obtaining an outlet to the sea that enables them to by-pass the Suez Canal, which Egypt has closed to them. Consequently they built the port of Eilath out of nothing, on the western side of the head of the Gulf. It lies close to the site of Asiongaber, the town from which Solomon's fleet set sail to the wealthy shores of Arabia. The Jews have brought in water, constructed quays and installed hoisting equipment. An oil pipeline, which will bring the oil of the Persian Gulf right across the Negev to the very heart of Israel, is at present under construction. Linked by roads with Bersabee, Eilath has already grown into a small town, whose inhabitants live in comfort amid the most desert-like conditions imaginable. Finally, on the outskirts of the town, the Jews have prospected iron ore and manganese deposits, and especially copper deposits which have a 2 per cent pure metal content; and they intend to exploit these resources. Thus through their enthusiasm, tenacity and enterprise, the Jews have succeeded in bringing life to a region which at one time seemed doomed.

CHAPTER V

TRANSJORDAN

Of the four main areas of the Holy Land which I set out to describe, the last one, the plateauland of the Transjordan from the Djebel Druse to the Gulf of Akaba, is the largest. This is because it broadens out in the east in the direction of the South Arabian desert. It is also the most elevated of the four areas, for it was violently uplifted along the line of the Jordan fault. Overlooking the Middle Jordan, the Adjloun ridges rise to more than 4068 ft, and in the Kerak region on a level with the Lisan peninsula the altitude is 3280 ft, while in the Ma'an region overlooking the Araba it is 5577 ft. But these great altitudes are restricted to the extreme western edge of the platform, for the plateau dips steadily as it goes away eastward, where eventually we find the El Azraq basin less than 1640 ft in altitude.

These differences in elevation are of prime importance in the utilization of the country. The lofty western lip catches the rain clouds which have passed over the top of the lower-lying Judaea and Samaria. Precipitation here, then, is more plentiful than might be imagined despite the great distance from the sea. We have seen that on the plateaus it rains as much as on the hills of Palestine. Moreover, to a certain extent the height attenuates the fierceness of the summer heat. The climate up here is healthier than on the western plains. And so these "Mountains opposite", as the Jews of old used to call them, are not a bad place on the whole.

One must not generalize too much, however, because there are gradations: longitude and latitude cause considerable variations. As we move from north to south the rainfall decreases, and the folds of the 5577-ft Ma'an region receive much less rain than the Adjloun dome which is lower. Moreover, as the land slants eastward, humidity rapidly diminishes. These climatic characteristics give rise to three regional types arranged consecutively from west to east in Transjordan. The highest part of the plateau, about 30 miles in width, can pass for a good region, although it loses height as it goes southward. Adjacent to it in the east, there is a belt of steppe which is wider at the northern end, narrowing until it gradually disappears in the south. The steppe merges into desert on the far eastern side.

Two sub-regions can be distinguished in the western band where human settlements are located. North of the latitude of Jerusalem is the richest part of the plateau. The country south of this is poor.

This northern section is the Gilead district, inhabited in ancient times by a sect of the Jews, who observed strict rules, and whose task it was to defend Palestine against the Ammonites. They were a pious and conservative community, adhering faithfully to their religion and despising the Samaritans for their frequent lapses into idolatry. Their country was endowed with the perhaps best soils in the Holy Land in ancient times; the plains and broad ridges were covered with a fertile soil derived from calcareous decay. There is plenty of water; this is explained by the sufficiency of the rainfall and by the presence near the surface of underground water, which can be tapped by the wells or which feeds the little streams. This makes for an abundance of vegetation: on the edge of the tableland we find carobs, pistachio-trees and junipers, which give

way to the Mediterranean-type forest of small oaks, the
scene of Absalom's downfall.

These plateaus are cultivated, therefore: they were at
one time the granary of Palestine. Farming is carried out
mainly by small peasant proprietors, while other peasants
work for town-dwellers: sometimes they are strangers to
the district, or Arab refugees who sold their land to the
Jews. The peasants live in large villages grouped together
for protection—a necessary precaution—for the pilfering
Bedouin are not far away, and there is also the necessity of
not going too far away from the water supply. The small
houses, built of unfired brick, and sometimes of stone,
are flat-roofed. They are composed in the case of the
poorer inhabitants of a single room divided by a partition:
the family lives on one side of it and the livestock on the
other. The houses of the well-to-do peasants include a
separate outhouse for animals and a room for guests; these,
together with the main building, are arranged around a
courtyard. Where the district is sufficiently supplied with
water to allow for extra watering, the village is encircled
by an orchard. Beyond this, the fields begin; sometimes
they are only a few yards wide and of an unbelievable
length. The swing plough is used for tilling them. Tractors
and metal ploughs are just beginning to make their appearance in this region.

The chief crops on these northern plateaus are cereals,
and in particular wheat, cultivated by dry-farming methods
with a fallow season. Methods are poor, and the abundance
of weeds in the fields presents a sorry sight. Despite the
soil's fertility, yields are low, rarely reaching 10 quintals
per hectare (approx. 8 cwt per acre). The peasants also
grow tobacco; this would be a lucrative occupation if the
process of curing the leaves were not so poor. The slopes
bear vines, olives and figs, and these are not very productive, especially since they were attacked by phylloxera.

Lastly, the farmer keeps livestock. But here cattle are not numerous: they are used together with donkeys for drawing the plough. The herds are those of sheep, and especially goats—the dreaded enemy of the forester.

After the harvest has provided for the needs of the peasant, there remains a surplus, particularly of wheat. But the towns have also to be fed, and there are many of them on these northern plateaus. They are strung out along the great thoroughfare that stretches from Syria to the south and which runs on the tableland without a break except for the deep canyon of Wadi Zerka, which cuts through the plateau to its base. In the north there is Irbid (23,000 inhabitants), the regional centre of the richest area, a centre for wheat and tobacco. In the Adjloun area there are the large villages of Adjloun and Djerach; then the small centre of Es Salt situated on the Jerusalem–Amman road, and lastly there is Madaba in the south. But all these are overshadowed by the capital of the kingdom—Jordan–Amman.

Amman has a long history behind it. It was called Rabbat-Ammon, when a Ptolemaic king, Ptolemy II Philadelphus, changed its name to Philadelphia and rebuilt it. The ruins of a Greek theatre still stand here. In the old city the white houses stand packed together on the gentle slopes of a valley which dips away slowly eastward to the desert. The altitude, 2361 ft, provides a less oppressive climate here than that of the rift valley. Amman was for a long time the chief town of its region, and later developed into the capital of the Hashemite kingdom. Later it grew further still as a result of the influx of Arab refugees, who today make up 40 per cent of its 120,000 population. And living conditions have become very cramped, in order to absorb the extra population. The town now has eight persons per house. But on top of that 29 per cent of these refugees live in tents and 8 per cent have found a dwelling-place in caves. Thus, out of the 90,000 refugees who crossed the Jordan, the largest number stayed in Amman; the other towns received only a few (at Adjloun they comprise a mere 14 per cent of the total population, while in other places the proportion is less still), and the remainder dispersed over the country districts. The burden of the refugee problem is not felt so keenly here as in Judaea and Samaria.

It is in the towns that the small amount of industry is located. Amman accounts for 40 per cent of the kingdom's total industrial labour force, and this includes the territory west of the Jordan. The industries are mainly home-based: they produce metal instruments, intricate hand-made ornaments, and there is some cotton and wool weaving. The only real factories are in Amman: a factory for processing dairy produce, two cigarette factories, a tannery and a factory for producing rouge. And lastly, at a short distance from the city, at Ruseifa, there is an Anglo-Jordanian Company which in 1937 began to extract a very pure type of tricalcium phosphate with a 70 to 75 per cent concentration. These workings are very prosperous and the annual production amounts to more than 150,000 tons.

This phosphate commands a good price. Moreover, the mines are close to the so-called Mecca railway, which links up in the north with the Syrian railroad system at Deraa. From Deraa it would be easy to reach Haifa. But the Deraa–Haifa line has been cut since 1948. And now, in order to reach external markets, the phosphate has to be taken as far as Damascus and thence to Beirut, with the additional transport costs that this involves. These costs are high and the export trade feels the effects. The same is true of the potash extracted at the Kallia works on the shores of the Dead Sea. This is taken by lorry to Amman along the new, direct highway that links the city to

Jerusalem. But transport from there onward is particularly troublesome.

The northern tableland is on the whole a region equipped with genuine natural resources, both agricultural and mineral; also the tide of Arab refugees has not had quite the same devastating effect here as it has had on Judaea and Samaria. But it is in a state of semi-paralysis through being cut off from its natural outlet which is the Palestine coast. And these conditions are reproduced all along the southern extension of the plateau-land and are further aggravated by climatic influences.

As one goes south there is a decrease in humidity, and this is accompanied by a gradual narrowing of the fertile belt. Grain crops are still grown, but they are largely dependent on the seasons. Barley has now replaced wheat as the staple crop. Human settlements are confined to the hollows, for it is in these places that a little water can be tapped from the underground resources. There is also a thinning out in the numbers of trees, and desert plants now come into contact with those of the Mediterranean type. Human conditions also alter: many peasants here are without land of their own, while the great landowners, the sheiks, own enormous amounts of land. For example, there are the Houeitat, strung out between Ma'an and Akaba in the south: in about twenty villages here the land is owned by about twenty individuals.

Yet this change for the worse to be observed in natural conditions on these plateaus as we move south, shows variations that man has discerned from all times. In the north, from Madaba to the deep canyon of the Arnon, there is the Belka district, still more or less inhabited. After the Arnon there is the Moab plateau looking down on to the Dead Sea; here man is leaving the ridges and forming settlements at the heads of the valleys that descend to the rift and there they cultivate the red earth. In the

Middle Ages, Moab was sufficiently populated and cultivated for the Crusaders to make considerable efforts to defend it against the pillaging bands from the desert. This gave rise to the fine Frankish fortress of Kerak, still surrounded by a sizeable township, and that of Montreal (Chobak), the scene of the exploits of Renaud de Roussillon, the terror of the Arabs. Further south we come to Edom, whose plateaus become increasingly desert-like; so much so that the human centres have retreated to the floor of the very deep, narrow valleys that slope down to the Araba. These gorges that have been carved right through the plateau to an abysmal depth present a fantastic sight. The water, however, hardly flows more than once or twice per year at the bottom of these chasms. But it is obvious that during the Quaternary the periods of rain provided enough water to enable the torrents to accomplish their formidable task. These valleys have cut right through the limestone of the plateau and into the richly hued Petra sandstone. Where the different strata meet is also the place where springs arise; and these in their turn have caused the establishment of villages carrying on a terrace cultivation. There was once even a town here—Petra, which still exists today in the form of a large village. Its presence is explained by the existence of the highway of antiquity which went down to Egypt, avoiding the Dead Sea and crossing the Araba valley at the part where it is elevated. The Nabataeans, who were a nation of caravaneers, originally set up their warehouses here. These peace-loving tribes, when searching for a defensible site for storage depots, found the high ground unsuitable, as it was too arid, and so chose a deep chasm. The floor of the chasm, after widening out, closes in again at both ends into two gorges of remarkable narrowness, which could easily be blocked in the face of an enemy. And so Petra flourished, even becoming under Roman rule the capital of the province of Arabia. Its magnificent buildings carved out of the living rock are the most striking archeological sight in the Holy Land.

And so the western edge of the plateau merges into desert in the south. It is not the sole useful part of Transjordan, for it is flanked on its eastern side by a belt of steppe, where human life continues to be possible.

As the terrain slants gently eastward, after the watershed between the Jordan and Arabian depressions, there is a decrease in precipitation accompanied by an increase in temperature, and so aridity is increasingly felt. Trees disappear and the region is given up to grass, which withers as soon as spring is over. In the broad valleys, the wadis bear water only on a few occasions in winter.

Yet is is possible to turn these poor conditions to profit; in ancient times the steppe was put to use and populated. The ruins dating back to Hellenistic and Roman times testify to the fact, as well as the numerous tells that are scattered over the region. It is possible to build small dams across the valley lines in order to collect the flood waters; to sink wells through the alluvial deposits and thus tap the water table; also to bore tunnels underneath the alluvial slopes and provide them with openings to the surface, after the manner of the foggaras in the Sahara: the local name for them here is qanats. Some of these works have been brought back into use. Jordan is in fact trying to repopulate this belt which was inhabited not long ago. But the peasants found here are not the sturdy peasant proprietors of Irbid or Djerach, but Bedouin who have settled down permanently and who now live as serfs to feudal overlords possessing vast tracts of land. They grow a little barley and a few vegetables; they keep sheep, goats and camels.

The steppe belt possesses, however, a great advantage which could earn for it a very profitable rôle in the

economy. Running along it is the Mecca railway, built
by Turkey at the beginning of the century. The line
keeps away from the western tableland, which is richer,
however, in order to avoid the difficulties of crossing the
gorges which cut the plateau on their way to the Rift
valley. The railway-line has many small forts along it
(Qalaat), built for defence against the Bedouin. It has
even been responsible for the growth of the large village
of Ma'an out of what had been originally a desert
oasis. But since the expulsion of the Hashemites from
Arabia, effected by the Wahabis, the line has been cut
beyond Ma'an. Also, it goes no further north than
Damascus and Beirut, as already stated. Consequently
the railway's economic rôle is drastically curtailed and
it suffers the consequences of this. It is all the more
unfortunate that it is so little utilized, because of the
rich phosphate deposits which have been found at El
Hasa close to the line a little north of Ma'an. It is un-
thinkable that these phosphates should have to be taken
right up to Beirut. And so the decision has been taken
to open up for the kingdom a fresh outlet in the south
by constructing a road which will enable lorries to reach
the sea at Akaba, a medium-sized port where work has
begun on improving the facilities.

Like the fertile belt, the steppe belt narrows towards
the south, until it finally disappears altogether even
before Ma'an. In the east it merges into desert; but it is
a desert less awe-inspiring than the Sahara. It has a surface
gently sloping eastwards, with slight undulations, and
crossed by shallow valleys which converge from the north,
east and south-east towards the enclosed hollow of Azraq,
or towards the even more low-lying depression of Sirhan.
In these valleys, the wadis may bring a few spates every
winter, and thereby feed the superficial strata which can

readily be tapped by means of wells. This is the region where the true Bedouin live and wander.

The number of the Transjordan Bedouin is not known exactly. It can be said that they number between 100,000 and 120,000. Until quite recently, they were truly nomadic, staying during the winter in the desert in search of pastures, and approaching the western regions in summer, and even coming into them. But the advance of modern civilization into western Transjordan, however rudimentary in form it may be, cannot put up with the annual migration of nomads. Gradually they have been checked and restricted. The result today has been that the numbers of Bedouin actually living as nomads have greatly fallen. It is set at 40,000 at the most. The rest have become half-sedentary, living in the steppe belt, engaging in a very small amount of farming and pasturing their herds. From these are recruited men for the Arab Legion; the Bedouin are still the most loyal supporters of the Hashemite dynasty.

CHAPTER VI

CONCLUSION

In concluding this survey of the various aspects of the Holy Land, it can be said that it is not a country particularly well endowed with natural advantages.

Its physical structure is not noticeably forbidding, of course, apart from the Jordan rift which presents an obstacle to communications between the different parts of the country. But it is situated on the edge of the arid zone, and on account of its latitude it would be a desert, were it not bordered on the west by the Mediterranean, which is its sole provider of moisture. It is only in the cool season, however, that moisture is brought, and there is a steady decline from north to south in the amount provided. Therefore, the problems of agriculture are complex and difficult ones. Water must be obtained and then utilized by various means. The hillsides must be provided with low walls; unhealthy marshland must be drained. All this does not make for an easy life. Indeed the Holy Land is a country where conditions are harsh.

And so it might well be imagined that the Holy Land could hardly arouse the envy of others. But on its southern and eastern borders it is flanked by lands that have even less to show, and which are little more than deserts or semi-deserts. To the unfortunate inhabitants of these countries, the Holy Land seems like a paradise. The Semitic nomads who have wandered through these lands have always been tempted to make their way into the Holy Land. And so all through the ages, it has been a kind of besieged camp, and we know what fierce struggles the Hebrews had to wage in order to repel the Ammonites, Moabites and Edomites.

But there is another, more serious, factor, which arises as a result of the geographical position of the Holy Land. It is the place where Asia meets Africa. Thus it has always lain in the path of the invaders going from one continent to the other. On several occasions the Egyptians extended their rule over the Holy Land in order to secure access to the forests of the Lebanon, whose timber they needed for their navy. Most of the invaders, however, appeared from the eastern interior, where Asia seemed inexhaustible in her resources of people. Their inroads can be traced right from the dawn of history. As they went, they massacred, pillaged, razed and abducted. Fresh populations came with them, and the original neolithic population received influxes of Armeniac-type newcomers from the north, Canaanites, Aramites and Jews.

However, the geographical rôle fulfilled by the Holy Land as a means of communication did not have the same historical effect on her various regions. The principal thoroughfares lay along the outside edges. The chief of these was that running along the coastal plain and through the Jezreel valley, thus providing access to Syria. The other main route ran along the Transjordan plateau, avoiding the Rift valley and leading directly to the rich lands of Arabia. As a result, a kind of natural fastness was formed between the two highways, and the successive waves of invasion swept past hardly touching it. This is particularly true of the highlands to the south, where the Dead Sea provides a moat to protect the rear against any attack. And so those tribes which succeeded in gaining possession of the harsh Judaean ridges after long struggles escaped being engulfed in the tides of invasion and

CONCLUSION **81**

managed, if not to preserve their independence, at least to retain their identity. This nation was able to evolve freely, shut away from foreign influences on these high plateaus, whose very poverty was a form of protection in itself, and it was thus able to secure that individuality which makes it an almost unique people in the history of the world.

The irresistible might of Rome put an end to such proud isolation and destroyed the nation of God, dispersing it to all corners of the ancient world. With the weakening of Roman power, the Holy Land once more fell a victim to the recurring scourge of invasion. One after the other, Persians, Arabs, Mongols, Franks, Egyptian or Baghdad sultans occupied and ravaged it until it finally fell beneath the sway of the Ottoman Turks. With the establishment of the British Mandate, there was room for hope that at last peace would be restored. But the British phase proved to be a period when the country was torn by faction, during which Jewish colonies were established and finally the State of Israel was founded by force of arms.

At present we see a Holy Land divided up between two hostile States: Israel and the Jordanian kingdom. Israel has secured the better portion: Galilee—the coolest region; the plains—the most fertile and easily developed region; that section of the Rift where there is fresh water, namely Houleh and Lake Tiberias. But she has also accepted a very poor region, the enormous Negev desert, which makes up more than half the area of its territory. The Jordanian kingdom has not succeeded so well: although it received the Transjordan plateaus, whose topography is not too bad, and the ridges of Samaria, which are also not too bad, it has inherited the largest portion of Judaea, which is harsher, and the scorched tracts of the Ghor.

But the situation has become absurdly complicated with the drawing up of Israel's frontiers. From the hilltops of

Upper Galilee it runs north to take in a small enclave, a few miles in width, projecting between Syria and the Lebanon. Then it just fails to circumscribe the whole of Lake Tiberias, after which it takes in the right side of the Ghor as far as Beisan. Next, turning west, the frontier approaches the coastal plain, squeezing Israel up against the sea. It now ascends the plateaus and reaches Jerusalem, and then drops down to the Dead Sea. In the south-west it skirts the Gaza Strip, even though Gaza is a Palestinian town. The border thus cuts indiscriminately across valleys and uplands, truncates highways, tracks and railway-lines. And this frontier is no mere formality, the concern of a handful of customs officials. It is bristling with military defences: over the entire length there are emplacements with heavy and light automatic weapons, and mortars. Hardly a week goes by without an exchange of shots between the two sides. The saddest sight of all is that of a Jerusalem split into two sectors by a no-man's-land guarded by lookout slits, sandbags and weapons permanently pointing at the enemy.

The success achieved by Israel under conditions such as these is worthy of admiration. On the small territory, which had scarcely a million inhabitants in 1920, Israel has built up a modern State with a population of 2,331,000 in 1963; out of this number there are 263,000 non-Jews (11 per cent). The population in 1949 was only 1,174,000, and, despite the favourable demographic conditions—a birth-rate of 26·9 and a mortality of 5·7 per 1000—two-thirds of this remarkable increase in population are due to immigration, originating from Europe, Asia and Africa. The immigrants had to be settled, formed into true citizens and given the same ideals; they also had to be instructed and trained. This constituted a great undertaking and a great achievement.

Making use of her ill-assorted manpower, Israel has

transformed those regions which she succeeded in winning. The swamps have been drained, and the parched areas watered. The Nazzaz crusts in the subsoil have been broken up; on the hillsides terraces have been excavated. Everywhere water has been sought out, collected, directed and distributed; the most astonishing undertaking is the 124-mile-long National Water Carrier which brings water, pumped from Lake Tiberias, to the parched but fertile soil of the Negev. Chemical fertilizers are everywhere lavished on the cultivated land. A judicious choice of crops is made, to meet market requirements, and the best agricultural methods are employed in farming them. The mechanization of agriculture is well advanced: there are 7000 tractors in use at present. Other spheres of development are not being neglected. In three years Israel constructed 1013 miles of new roads. The length of railway line has increased from 100 to 400 miles. An Israeli merchant navy has been created, and recently an ocean-going passenger liner was added to its fleet. The Port of Haifa handles 2,500,000 tons. An industry has been built up whose variety continues to grow and whose production tends to meet local needs and at the same time provides an export trade. The Jewish State today enjoys a standard of living comparable to that of West European nations, and this in a country which is reduced to a width of 16 miles at its centre, with its frontiers perpetually under threat, and where the farm-worker has his rifle and grenades within easy reach while he works.

The other State, the Jordanian kingdom, is completely different. It takes in, on the left of the Rift valley, the tableland of Transjordan as far as the desert, and in the west pushes Israel back by means of two massive bulges, one in the north, the other in the south, namely Samaria and most of Judaea. The country itself is not lacking in resources, with its grain-crop farming, its olives and vines, and its herds and mineral deposits. But it is burdened with various serious disadvantages.

In the first place, the country has remained a backward country, one which has not adopted the standards of modern civilization. Consequently, agriculture, the basic wealth of the region, has remained fixed in its traditional patterns; there is little or no knowledge of crop rotations, chemical fertilizers, mechanization and animal management. The returns of Jordanian agriculture have remained low. Also, the peasants are often crippled by the heavy rents that they have to pay to absentee landlords. Despite efforts that were made during the British Mandate, industry is still weak. The volume of trade is very low, as there is not much to sell, and little money with which to buy; also because of the lack of roads and the poor state of the rail communications, and finally because Jordan is being literally choked by her frontiers.

Indeed, the kingdom is deprived of all outlets by which it could easily communicate with the outside world, on account of the absurd frontier, which reflects the *de-facto* front-line situation following the bitter fighting between Jordan and Israel. The Jerusalem–Jaffa road is blocked at the Mandelbaum Gate; the railway line between Nablus and Haifa is cut after Jenin, while the line that ran from Deraa to the sea is cut before it reaches Lake Tiberias. The Lebanon ports are a long way away, and Syria has imposed transit restrictions. There remains only the distant port of Akaba, therefore, hundreds of miles away across the desert. As a result, Jordan's trade is paralysed by these difficulties.

Lastly, the kingdom is badly hit by the flood of refugees who left Israel. A UNESCO commission put their numbers in 1954 at 350,000; this figure seems a low one. In any case, today they number at least 400,000 owing to the increase from new births. An energetic, modern State is easily capable of absorbing and benefiting from a massive influx of refugees, as West Germany did after the war. But such people become an almost intolerable burden to a State that is badly organized. This is all the truer in Jordan's case because here they comprise almost one-third of the kingdom's total population of 1,450,000 inhabitants, and also because they have concentrated in large numbers in the territory west of the Jordan, where they amount to almost a half of the population. Add to this the fact that this region could scarcely provide enough sustenance for its indigenous population, even before the arrival of the refugees. Few of these newcomers have found a way of integrating themselves into the Jordanian economy, and most of them owe their meagre subsistence to the aid provided by international organizations. Their destitution is a breeding-ground for rancour and hatred, which, although directed against Israel, constitutes nevertheless an embarrassment for the kingdom. The refugees are constantly fomenting trouble and accusing the passivity of the Jordanian Government, and they would be actively subversive were it not for the presence of the Arab Legion, whose numbers are recruited from among loyal Bedouin.

And so on one side we have Israel—a dislocated State, strangled, surrounded by her enemies, yet prosperous and dynamic; while on the other side we see Jordan, poor, shut in, perpetually disturbed by the protests of the embittered refugees. The only contact between the two takes the form of border incidents which are settled by bullets. This is the bewildering spectacle which the Holy Land presents today. It is to be hoped that the hatred between the two factions will die down, as it seems to have done in Galilee, and that Jordan might relinquish her pan-Arab dreams and allow herself to be helped by Israel to become a modern State capable of providing honourably for all her subjects.

PART II

TOPOGRAPHY AND ANIMAL LIFE

by

M. DU BUIT, O.P.

Editor's note. In order to bring the land of the Old and New Testaments vividly before our eyes Fr du Buit, O.P., formerly professor at the École Biblique in Jerusalem, recalls here, by description and diagram, several important geographical facts which could not find a place in M. Blanchard's general description.

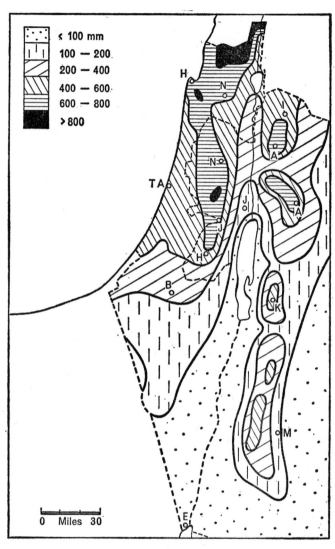

ANNUAL DISTRIBUTION OF RAINFALL

CHAPTER VII

REGIONAL LANDSCAPE

FEATURES

LANDSCAPE FEATURES OF PALESTINE

External land forms are governed by their geological structure, by erosion, and ultimately by climate. In fact the last mentioned exerts predominant influence.

Desert climate

We can adopt the same isohyet that will also be valid for vegetation, namely that of a maximum annual rainfall of 4 ins. Under these conditions, erosion by water is low or non-existent, and so the land surfaces are not altered very much. The wind carries away only small amounts of material. The change from day to night temperatures causes the rocks to split, and as a result the mountain-sides are clad with great falls of loose rocks, which a little rain binds together where they lie. The morphology of the Palestinian deserts, therefore, is characterized by slightly tilted plateaus, ending in steep or precipitous sides. At high altitudes the rock is laid bare, while lower down it has a covering (fig. a).

However, where the slope is very abrupt and at the same time the rock is soft, the erosive action of water is no longer insignificant. Such is the case in the Judaean wilderness in particular: here we see mountains that are deeply ravined, with their edges chiselled and indented. And it is difficult to distinguish the debris, which is broken down into very fine material, from the parent-rock (fig. b). In the Transjordan desert there is no erosion, but on the other hand the sand deposited by the wind chokes the relief, whose original structure was not very strongly marked in the first place.

Humid climates

Here the action of water is predominant, but its effects depend on the quality of the rock.

The Cenomanian-Turonian rocks are fairly pure limestone, with a fine grain, hard on the surface but fissured inside. While a certain amount of the water trickles down the outside without having any great effect, the remainder soaks into the rock and drains out of it at the bottom. Erosion here occurs as a result of internal disintegration: within the rock mass, erosion hollows out caves and underground rivers, and on plateaus it forms basins. Where they rise, springs carve deep, sheer-walled canyons. The main block of the mountain departs little from its original surface relief, and retains its massive appearance. This is observable in the central chain of hills in Palestine, as well as in Galilee and Mount Carmel, where quite a large number of fine grottoes have been found. The central plateau in such mountain blocks is level, dominated by inconspicuous summits, and covered with hollows in which fertile soil has collected. These are suitable localities for human habitation and movement. The valleys are too narrow to be used for cultivation, and too precipitous and constricted to serve as thoroughfares; in fact they usually form obstacles to human movement (fig. c).

The rocks of the Senonian and Tertiary are loose grained, and absorb a large amount of water, which has

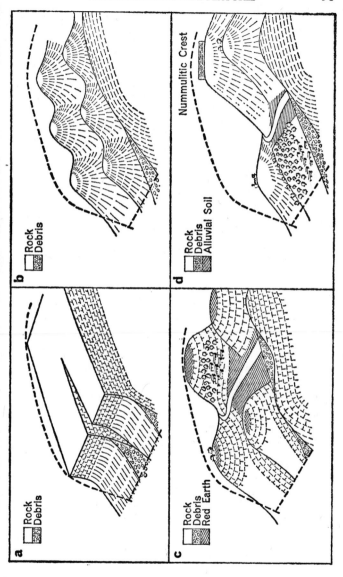

the effect of rendering them soft. The internal fissures become blocked, and so there is no subterranean flow of water. Erosion in this case is principally surface erosion produced by flowing water. Although these mountains are a little younger than the others, their morphology has gone further: their surface relief shows a greater divergence from its original form. The highlands are sharply divided up into individual crests and summits, each of which takes on the appearance of a small mountain. Broad valleys with gently sloping sides, which are easy to cultivate, open out towards the plains. These become the centres of human activity. This type of morphology is best illustrated by the Samaritan basin. It is also to be found, though on a lesser scale, in certain parts of Lower Galilee, for example in the Nazareth hills. The characteristics outlined above are mitigated by a decrease in altitude (fig. d).

RAINFALL AND CLIMATE

Palestine is subject to various climatic influences. The only constant factor is the two-season cycle with a dry summer alternating with a winter during which all the rain falls. Rainfall of the half seasons—September and October on the one hand, April and May on the other—when there is any, accounts for a very low percentage of the total: 2 to 8 per cent for spring and 4 to 12 per cent for autumn. Since the winters are subject to complex influences it is not surprising that the annual amount of rain varies between the normal and an amount twice the normal, even within a long climatic period.

Distribution of temperatures

The hills of the coastal fringe have their own local climate, which grows cooler the higher the altitude. But these hills are not extensive enough to act as a cold mass in relation to the neighbouring regions. They merely limit

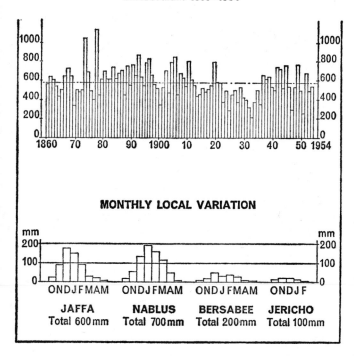

ANNUAL VARIATION IN RAINFALL
JERUSALEM 1860-1954

MONTHLY LOCAL VARIATION

the mitigating influence of the sea. In the hinterland the winters are dominated by the cold mass of the Armenian mountains, and the summers by the warm mass of the Mesopotamian plain.

Local distribution of rainfall

In accordance with general meteorological laws it rains more on the side of a mountain exposed to the wind than on the sheltered side, and more on the high parts than the

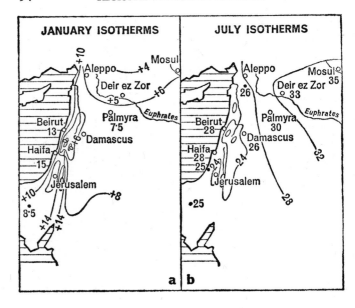

low, and, as regards the region now under study, more in
the north than in the south. The resultant distribution of
rainfall is shown for Palestine on p. 88 and for the whole
of the Near East in fig. c, p. 95. Owing to the fact that
the landscape relief lies in bands perpendicular to the
general direction of the moist winds, the contrasts between
neighbouring regions can be very sharp: it is possible to go
from a humid region to a desert one in a space of 18 miles.
It is interesting to make a comparison with western
Europe. Rome receives $31\frac{1}{2}$ ins. of rain; London $24\frac{1}{2}$; Paris
$22\frac{1}{2}$; Madrid $16\frac{1}{2}$. It would be, therefore, untrue to say
simply, without qualifying the statement, that the climate
of the Palestine mountains is dry. If it differs from that of
the European seaboards, the difference lies in the rate of
precipitation and not in the absolute amount.

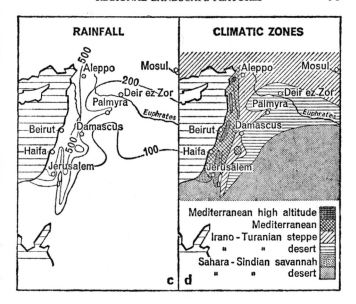

Climatic zones

Developing these observations, we can distinguish the following climatic zones in the Near East (fig. d):

Mediterranean climate is dominated by marine influence. Rainfall exceeds 19½ ins. The temperature range is moderate: at Jerusalem the winter average is 9° C (48° F), and this allows a few days of snow; the summer average is 24° C (75° F). This climatic zone extends over the whole of the coastal range exposed to the wind, up to an altitude of about 3280 ft. In the higher altitudes, precipitation rises to and exceeds 39 ins., and the winters are really cold; precipitation is long-lasting and, in places, continuous. On the sea coast from Haifa to Tripoli, the contrast between sea and mountains produces air circulation in which the cold waves do not touch the ground. I have no detailed explanation for such a phenomenon, but there are other places with similar conditions. The winters then become very mild, and the summers hot, with the air loaded with humidity. The climate tends towards the tropical type.

The Irano-Turanian climate is the dry, continental kind. Annual rainfall remains below 19½ ins. The winters are cold: Aleppo and Mosul have an average of 6° C (42° F), which signifies a certain amount of frost. There have been occasions when the Tigris has frozen over at Mosul. The summers are hot: Mosul has an average of 35° C (95° F); Aleppo is more moderate with 26° C (78° F). The difference between day and night temperatures is about 10° C (50° F) in winter, and 20° C (68° F) in summer. This is the climate of the plains of Syria and Upper Mesopotamia, and their extension into Transjordan. Adjacent deserts have winters that are cold and still comparatively humid; they get on average more than 4 ins. of rain.

The Sahara-Sindian climate is the desert type, with warm winters and very low amounts of rain—less than 4 ins. This climate belongs to central Arabia, Sinai—excluding high areas—and also to the Jordan valley. It merges by a series of slight gradations into the Irano-Turanian climate. A small transitional zone that might be termed Sahara-Sindian savannah lies on the fringe of the Mediterranean mountain range, and especially at the southern end of the Palestine coastal plain.

METEOROLOGICAL CONDITIONS

Summer situation

The depression zone over the Indian Ocean extends over the Persian Gulf and Mesopotamia. Periodically a small, local depression over Cyprus replaces it. Circling around this cyclone are air masses coming from the Caucasus region, and arriving from a westerly direction on the Syro-

Palestinian coastline. This is a circulatory movement from the Indian Ocean monsoon. The air masses arrive after being cooled by their passage over the Black Sea and the Mediterranean, and they are charged with a certain amount of humidity. Over the whole of the hill regions, there is abundant night dew; in the Lebanon and Galilee, whose high ground rises more closely to the sea, heavy cloud condensation is observed in the middle of the day, but never any rain. The result is that summer here, from about June to September, is quite a pleasant season in spite of the daytime heat. Trees grow and bear fruit, and certain crops may be grown without irrigation.

Intermediate situation: the "khamsin"

This is a spring or early autumn situation. The Mesopotamian depression is not in operation, and high-pressure centres over the continental masses to the east and west. Between the two, the coastal regions are crossed by small depressions passing from south to north; these attract warm air masses from Africa or Arabia. In Palestine, the "khamsin" is a light wind which often veers quite quickly. It often bears dust that it has gathered up from the Sahara or Arabian desert. This wind may also bring with it clear air, with very low amounts of cloud, coming perhaps from tropical Africa. In the hill regions, the khamsin can destroy the fruit crop, which is in the process of setting at this time. On the inland steppes, it can ruin the cereal harvest.

The first heavy rain at the end of autumn

High pressure extends widely over the continent from the east, and low pressure over the maritime regions in the west. Masses of cold, moist air coming in from the North Atlantic reach the coast from a westerly and south-westerly direction. The sharp difference in temperature between this air and the land with which it enters into

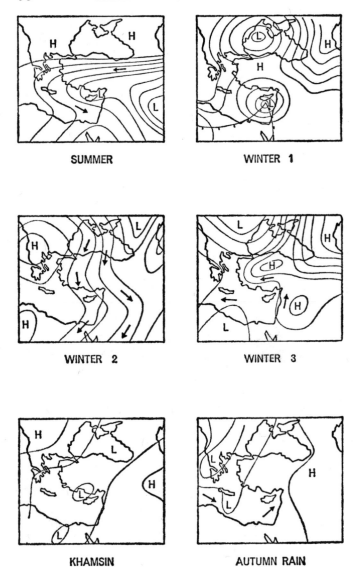

SUMMER

WINTER **1**

WINTER **2**

WINTER **3**

KHAMSIN

AUTUMN **RAIN**

contact produces unstable conditions, resulting in very heavy precipitation which may even cause damage.

Winter 1

A small depression from the west comes into the eastern Mediterranean. This is accompanied by a mild, humid wind which blows from south-west to north-east, freshening a little as it goes. The air mass originates in the Mediterranean or central Atlantic; its temperature is not a great deal different from that of the land. Unstable conditions are not necessarily set up with it; in this case there is at least a heavy dew at night, from which plant life benefits.

Winter 2

A large depression develops over the Black Sea or the Caspian. It sends southwards cold, humid polar air masses which give heavy rain or snow.

Winter 3

Zones of high pressure cover the whole of the Asian land mass as far as the coast, and send westward a cold, dry wind. This situation never lasts more than a few days at a time.

CHAPTER VIII

VEGETATION AND
WILDLIFE

VEGETATION

In every climatic zone, the natural vegetation has been partly replaced with farming crops.

In the Mediterranean zone, the natural plant cover is forest—very much the same as that to be found in Europe. The most prominent trees are the pine and evergreen oak. Forest degenerates into scrub, in which low trees form dense thickets; and these include species that are found in undergrowth: laurel, broom, lentisk, myrtle, and wild fruit trees such as the arbutus. Also worthy of mention is the Judas-tree. Some of these trees attain a fine growth in solitary conditions: for example the terebinth and carob.

The scrub degenerates into moorland, less dense and lower in height. Here we have the lavender, the rock-rose and dwarf bushes, such as the thorny burnet, thyme, marjoram, etc. This intermediate plant cover seems to hold its own more easily on sandy or clayey and chalky soils, which retain a certain amount of moisture close to the surface. On permeable rock, the destroyed forest is immediately replaced by a covering of bushes similar to those found in the Irano-Turanian steppe. This is due to the average altitude which causes cooler winters, and to the behaviour of flowing water, resulting in the drying out of the surface.

At higher altitudes, between 3280 and 6560 ft, the climate once supported forests of tall trees: cedars and junipers, taking the place of oaks. Some examples of these trees are still to be seen in the Lebanon. In hilltop regions, or after deforestation, there is a flora made up of sparse, low bushes, some of which are associated with the Mediterranean region, and others with the Irano-Turanian region.

The natural vegetation of the Irano-Turanian steppe is a tall, thick grass covering in spring. Graminaceous varieties are found represented here, also different kinds of wild cruciferous plants. Some plants resist arid conditions a little longer, in particular many kinds of thistle, which often cover the whole landscape. There are also corm plants: iris, crocus, liliaceous plants, which go through the summer and reform their leaves in the following season. Lastly, numerous types of small bush send down their roots quite deeply into the ground in order to reach the permanent moisture, and some of these resist the local type of plough and infest the fields. The steppe has hardly any trees on it. The only ones worth mentioning are thinly planted groups of pistachio and, on the fringe of the forest zone, oak. A variety of poplar and several species of willow grow in proximity to water.

The Irano-Turanian desert zone presents a vegetation similar in kind to the one we have just described, but here it is lower and less thick. Among the annual plants, there are graminaceous varieties, and among the permanent bushes we find wormwood. Plants now appear which are full of salt or bitter sap, and are thereby protected against evaporation; thus they are at the same time suited to the salt-impregnated soils. The waterside vegetation here is the same as for the Irano-Turanian steppe above.

The Sahara-Sindian zone, with its mild winters, is even

poorer than the previous one. It has one or two particular
species of its own. The waterside vegetation is of an
African type, and includes several kinds of acacia, and
some "passion-flowers". The plant cover of the salt regions
is enlivened by the presence of many species: several
varieties of tamarisk, "Sodom apples", a fruit of fine
appearance, but empty inside, and also bitter colocynths.
Various grasses were formerly used for making soda, and
some trade even sprang up on account of it. On the seashore, the presence of ground water and the fairly heavy
dewfall provide enough moisture to support a real tree,
the "articulated tamarisk", which the Israelis have planted
in large numbers in the south. The eucalyptus, a recently
imported species from Australia, also flourishes in this
last of the climatic zones, as well as in all parts of the
Mediterranean zone, where the winter is not too cold for it.
It is associated with varieties of mimosa, which have also
been imported from Australia.

WILDLIFE

In addition to the animals that are native to the local
climatic zones, one also finds animals belonging to foreign
faunas, which have found their way here, namely, Euro-
Siberian and Sudano-Deccanian species. On account of its
small area, the Mediterranean zone does not possess any
large animal of its own. On the other hand, many animals
are able to adapt themselves to varied conditions, such
being the case with the best-known large mammals. Other
creatures are migratory, such as many birds and insects.
The subject of wildlife, therefore, can only be touched on
lightly here.

Mammals

The hare, lynx and fox can be considered as being
Mediterranean animals. The Irano-Turanian zone contains

another variety of fox, wild asses, such as were once known in the Transjordan desert, and numerous rodents which penetrate into all parts of the country. There are other, more localized rodents belonging to the Sahara-Sindian zone, and these include the spine-tailed mouse and the jerboa. The ibex holds its own in the rocks of the wilderness, and the gazelle and jackal are still widespread everywhere. There are still a few wolves left in the Lebanon. The stag was known here in antiquity; and it was only at the beginning of this century that the roebuck disappeared from the wooded areas. The bear, which seems to be holding out in the high mountains, is a native species. As for the wild boar, whose habitat is the banks of the Jordan, this belongs to the European, and not to the Egyptian variety. In ancient times, elephant roamed the swamps of Syria, and were hunted by the Pharaohs. Large antelope used to be found in the oases of the Araba, even in the early years of this century. The jungle thickets along the Jordan contained lions until the Middle Ages, and leopards frequented the wooded parts at the turn of the century. The striped hyena, which is still to be found in the less populated parts of the country, once existed everywhere.

Birds

The many species of migratory birds cannot be considered to be representative of the various climatic zones here. Only the stork can be mentioned on account of its beautiful outward passage in spring (its return journey takes it farther to the east); also we may mention the quail which summers in Europe and winters in central Africa: great flights of these birds cross Sinai and southern Palestine. It is a well-known fact that the spring flights of quail feed on hemlock, and sometimes to such an extent that their flesh becomes toxic through it.

It is impossible to consider, even in passing, all the 143 species of resident birds. The three climatic zones are well represented among this bird population. Tropical species are not numerous, and are restricted to the central ridge; while Euro-Siberian species are to be found only in Galilee. It has been observed several times that very closely related species of the same family are distributed in similar local climatic zones. Other examples reveal once more the close relationship existing between a species and a particular habitat, in spite of the small size of the country and the closely interwoven climatic zones in it.

Reptiles and Amphibia

Of the 83 known species, there are 32 Mediterranean, 30 Sahara-Sindian, 15 Irano-Turanian and 3 tropical species. These creatures adapt themselves to the climatic conditions here by restricting their activities to the hours when the temperature is suited to them, and consequently the coincidence of species with climatic zones becomes a little less precise. Among the 23 kinds of snake are several venomous species: the common Mediterranean viper, the horned viper, which belongs rather to the Irano-Turanian zone, and the tropical cobra, found in the Gaza oasis. There are 37 known species of lizards. Prominent among them is the gecko—a Mediterranean species of a tropical family. It is able to adapt to the parched conditions by leading a nocturnal existence, living among the rocks where the suction pads on its feet give it great agility. The gecko also penetrates readily into human dwellings. The chameleon is tropical in origin, but has adapted itself to the Mediterranean climate. Until the beginning of the century, crocodiles existed in the swamps of the Nahal Zarqa, the Israeli Nahal Ha-Tanninim. Several species of tortoise and amphibia are also known.

Fish

In the Jordan river system there are 30 species of fish: 12 Mediterranean, 6 Irano-Turanian, 3 Sahara-Sindian and 9 Sudano-Deccanian species. The last-mentioned are of the "spiny" type, so called on account of the comb-like form of their fins. Also there is the catfish (*Clarias lazera*) in which the historian Josephus recognized a Nile species.

Insects

More than 4000 species of insect have been established, but this figure falls far short of the total. The ecological facts, in so far as they have been studied up to the present, confirm the zonal division that has been adopted. I shall confine my remarks to a few of the more curious species. A species of Pieridae commonly known as the "cabbage white", migrate into the Palestine coastal plain at the beginning of winter, and there they breed until July, producing five generations. It appears that the strong heat kills them off, for nobody has ever seen the return journey of these migrants. A mosquito—the Mediterranean anopheles kind from Europe—finds its southern limit in Palestine: it lives exclusively in the always cool cisterns of houses and was responsible for the spread of malaria in the towns, until it was discovered and steps taken to combat it. The migratory locust inhabits the fringes of the Sudano-Deccanian and Sahara-Sindian zones. A study has been made in central Sudan of a large swarm of these. For reasons that are not yet clearly understood, the locusts begin at times to proliferate and change their appearance to some extent, and then enter a gregarious phase. The migration begins in September and moves across to the Red Sea shores, where a second generation of locusts may spring up if the autumnal rains are plentiful enough. A second migratory flight brings them into southern Palestine, where a third generation may hatch out if the end of the winter is sufficiently humid. From here they proceed to wreak havoc in the interior of the country. But the climate of both Arabia and the Palestinian desert is too irregular to permit this species to adopt those regions as a permanent habitat; at the same time the climate of the hills is too cold.

Of the entire insect population, 50 per cent belong to the Mediterranean fauna. This high figure is explained by the richness of the vegetation in this zone, for many insects depend very closely on a particular plant species for existence. The Irano-Turanian fauna and the Sahara-Sindian fauna each claim 15 per cent of the total.

Other Articulata

Three hundred and forty-five species of Arachnoids are known here; their distribution resembles that of the insects. Among them may be noted the Sahara-Sindian family of scorpions, of which there are six species in the Mediterranean and Irano-Turanian zoogeographical zones. Of these several are poisonous; in addition there are two poisonous spiders and one poisonous myriapod.

CHAPTER IX

AGRICULTURE

Cereals

Primitive, 14-chromosome wheat has been found growing in a state of spontaneous propagation in Palestine and Asia Minor, and must have been native to the Mediterranean and Irano-Turanian zones. It was cultivated in Europe in prehistoric times.

Of the 28-chromosome species, the bearded variety has also been found in Palestine and Iran; this came from a spontaneous mutation. This variety was cultivated in prehistoric times in Egypt and Mesopotamia, and remained in use in oriental and classical antiquity. The beardless, or bare-grain, varieties, the hard wheats, are culture-induced mutations which were unknown in the wild. In antiquity, as today, these are the principal cereals grown in the dry Mediterranean or Irano-Turanian climates.

The 42-chromosome group of wheats seem to have evolved by means of hybridization without any lowering of the chromosome number. Here, too, the bearded variety is known in the wild: it is spelt (German wheat); the beardless varieties are our ordinary soft wheats, which all prefer cooler and more humid climates. They were unknown in oriental antiquity, but were known as high-quality wheats in classical times.

Two-rowed barley is found growing in the wild in Palestine and neighbouring countries. Strains of four- and six-rowed barley are very old culture-induced mutations. All three species are still cultivated today. Barley has more modest requirements than wheat and has a faster growth; it has therefore been successfully introduced into the Irano-Turanian desert as far as the 4-in. isohyet, wherever there are favourable opportunities for it. In such regions, barley forms the base of human diet. In regions with a better climate, it constitutes an auxiliary crop or a means of soil enrichment.

Rice was imported as a crop at about the beginning of the Roman rule in Syria and Palestine, where it was cultivated on marshy land. A little is still to be seen in Syria. It does not seem to be a crop likely to spread, for in fact it is generally more profitable to utilize water more fully by spreading it over a greater area, and the present tendencies in artificial irrigation point this way.

The various strains of sorghum are much less demanding in soil and water, and are satisfied with the summer dewfall and the stocks of ground water stored in the deep soil of the valleys. This crop is another sideline, without any real economic importance. It was most likely introduced from Mesopotamia during the Roman occupation.

Grain crops make up a part of the diet today in the form of bread or ground corn, which is cooked with water; hard wheat semolinas and North African couscous are hardly, if at all, eaten today.

Pulses

Lentils have always been cultivated as field crops in the Mediterranean region. They seem to grow best on the plains or on hills of average altitude (about 1640 ft), where the winters resemble our springs. Higher up (2300 ft and more), the winters are too cold and are followed by a too intense summer drought, and so these crops are found more in the hills of Samaria than the Judaean highlands.

The bean has also been known from ancient times, but today is hardly grown except in gardens. The chick-pea was probably also an importation dating from the Roman period. Still more recent, as we know, are haricot beans. Some mention must also be made of different types of fodder vetches, including several whose fruit can be used for human consumption if need be. Several of them are native to the country, and the reason why the ancient texts seem unaware of their existence lies in their low value.

Industrial crops

Flax was formerly grown in Egypt and it has not been entirely abandoned there. It also grew under irrigation in the hot regions of Palestine, and in particular at Jericho (Josue 2. 6). Cotton, which has a higher yield, has replaced it everywhere since the Middle Ages. Although Egypt is, as we know, one of the main centres for cotton, the crop extends to Syria, where it is cultivated on the coastal plain and on the steppe between Homs and Aleppo. Mountainous soils are usually too unfertile to support it. The Israelis, for their part, are developing it as a crop on the coastal plains, including the Plains of Esdraelon and Acre. Hemp is still grown in places, and supplies a small craftsman's trade. It appears to have been known in ancient times in Mesopotamia, but was introduced into Palestine at a late date. Cane sugar appeared in the Middle Ages and was grown in irrigated gardens until about the eighteenth century. It has been completely abandoned and its place is being increasingly taken by sugar-beet, grown in the same regions as cotton. There seems to be no climatic reason to prevent both these crops from spreading into Arab Palestine, but it is questionable whether production there could justify the setting up of the necessary industrial plant. Sesame must have been brought here from Mesopotamia during the Roman period: it is cultivated nowadays under the same conditions as sorghum, its oil being used mainly as a condiment.

Vegetables

Potatoes are more highly appreciated by foreigners to the country than by natives; they are quite successfully grown on the plains and low hills, everywhere in fact where the winter is both mild and humid, rather like our spring. The cabbage and cauliflower, grown under similar conditions, are regularly sent by the Jordanians as items of export to Damascus and Beirut, and even to the oil countries. Small caravans of camels go through the countryside laden with cauliflowers, on their way to the forwarding centres. It is one of those unexpected sights which demonstrates that contact between different cultures and ways of life can be peaceful and profitable.

The water melon is much appreciated, and a big trade in this fruit is carried on between the Arab countries. It is grown as a field crop, and the harvest season, though quite short in duration, differs in date from country to country, and so each one imports and exports in turn.

The majority of the vegetables are grown in irrigated gardens; the season for each crop is staggered according to latitude and local climate. To find the majority of this produce on the market the whole of the year round is one of the delightful things about the Levant.

Trees

The olive is indigenous to the whole of the Mediterranean zone; it is, as we know, the best indication of the zone. It is capable of growing, if need be, on stony ground that is very deficient in plant soil, and so olive plantations can be widely extended to mountainous districts. This has been done on a large scale throughout the Arab countries of the East, ever since peaceful conditions were restored.

Indeed, this tree is as highly valued today as ever it was in ancient times.

The almond-tree is also a native of the Mediterranean, where it is found growing wild, but it also encroaches upon the more parched regions. The same is true of the pomegranate. The pistachio is Irano-Turanian, and today it is cultivated in the Aleppo region, where it is also found growing wild. It is unknown in Palestine. The carob-tree yields its fruit for fodder, but it can be eaten if necessary (Luke 15. 16). The present population does not value it very highly, and does not cultivate it systematically.

The fig-tree is probably not a native here, for its broad deciduous leaves point to a climate with humid summers. However, it is capable of bearing fruit in all parts of the Mediterranean mountainous regions, thanks to the summer dewfall of course, but it reaches complete growth only in watered gardens. Wild fig-trees are found, however; these are possibly cultivated trees that have reverted. The introduction of the fig-tree into Syria and Palestine certainly took place in prehistoric times. The prickly pear was recently imported from America.

The vine is native to the Mediterranean and Irano-Turanian regions, and wild varieties are also known. The climate most suited to the vine consists of a humid winter, which may be cold without any danger, followed by a dry summer with plenty of sun. These conditions reduce the risk of mildew and parasites, and cultivation can proceed with a minimum of care. This is the case in the whole of the hill country of Palestine, and especially at the higher altitudes (more than 2300 ft roughly); it is here that the indigenous viticulture is the most developed (cf. 2 Paral. 26. 10). In Greco-Roman times when the export trade was expanding, the vine was cultivated under irrigation on the plains and even at Jericho. This was made feasible thanks to the additional cares and skills familiar to the cultivators of classical antiquity, and it is being undertaken once again today.

The palm-tree may be considered as characteristic of the Sahara-Sindian region. Lower Mesopotamia has always been the centre for its cultivation. In Palestine, it is found at Jericho, where it was famous in ancient times; today we find it south of Tiberias, as well as on the coastal plain at Askalon and also farther south. The sycamore was once widespread over the plains and warm hills (1 Paral. 27. 28.[1] and Is. 9. 9); its fruit is very poor and it has ceased to be cultivated. There survive a few examples which have sown themselves.

The apple-tree, a European tree, thrives in the Lebanon mountains and also in the higher regions of Palestine (above 2620 ft). The pear is cultivated on a small scale, in spite of the absence of a wild variety. The apricot is very widespread in the Irano-Turanian region, and is cultivated especially in Syria, Damascus being the chief district for it. The peach is rare; and the plum-tree, which is grown at Damascus, has been adapted to the Palestine hill regions, where it was not altogether unknown before.

Among the citrus fruits, the citron was known in the latter years of the Second Temple when it was included in the liturgy of the Tabernacles. It is now no longer cultivated. Some of the other species of citrus were introduced in the Middle Ages and others more recently still. It was about the end of the eighteenth century that citrus-growing began to develop on the coastal plain, where it has both the sandy soil and mild climate that it requires; there are also good facilities here for artificial irrigation. The Israeli immigrants brought this branch of farming to a high degree of technical perfection, and it continues to expand thanks to their efforts. Citrus fruit is the country's

[1] The Vulgate reading is fig-trees. (Ed.).

only agricultural product which supports a lucrative export trade.

Last of all, the banana—originally an Indian fruit—was known already by Greek and Roman naturalists. The Arabs were probably responsible for effectively introducing it into Syria and Palestine during the Middle Ages. Bananas are now grown under irrigation on ordinary soils on the hot plains.

Steppe

Although the steppe often has the advantage of the large extent of its fertile land, it suffers the drawback of not offering a sufficiently wide variety of crops—except in irrigated gardens. The mountainous regions generally have less fertile soils, but they have the advantage of a wider range of crops. It may also have been observed that the innovations imported down the ages have always benefited the plains rather than the other regions. This is self-evident in the case of the tropical and sub-tropical ones, for these are strictly limited to the hottest parts of the country; it is also self-evident in the case of the industrial crops requiring deep, rich soils and large-scale production. Fruit-trees in mountainous districts, though more modest in their needs, are also less valuable economically, taken as a whole. Any future progress will be seen to emphasize further the unevenness; whether it be in the mechanization of work, which is successful only on the plains or plateaus, or whether it be in irrigation, which can be brought up only as far as the foothills. And so the economic balance of the various regions has been seriously upset, and will probably remain so. The same situation exists in all regions of the globe.

CHAPTER X

LIVESTOCK

Cattle

Out of all the domestic animals reared today, cattle are the only ones which appear to be native to the Holy Land. They probably originated from a small bovine species which is observed as early as the Paleolithic Age.

The present strain, therefore, adapted itself long ago to the climate, at the cost of a reduction in its size and yield. In the traditional pattern of farming, the animals are used primarily as draught animals, their milk and meat production being a sideline. Since they are very poorly fed on straw, it is only in spring that their coats take on a slightly glossy appearance. Stock-breeding is more success-ful in conditions where it is possible to move the cattle alternately between a marshy district, where, in the dry season, there is green fodder available, and a spring pasture for the wet season. This used to be the practice on the Plain of Sharon (1 Paral. 27. 29), and it is likely that the cattle of Basan spent their time between the Houleh marshes and the grassy plateaus of the Gaulan and Hauran. The water-buffalo, originally introduced from India, lives the whole year in swampland, and the draining of the latter is causing it to disappear; there are a few left in Syria.

The Israelis have succeeded in crossing the best native milch cow, the Damascus breed, with the black and white Frisian. They have thus obtained a cow with a good yield;

unfortunately it has to be fed on artificially irrigated pasture land.

Sheep

Contrary to common belief, sheep are not, it appears, indigenous animals here: there is no record of them in prehistoric times. The present strain, depicted and so vouched for by Assyrian art, must be a local mutational species of the fat-tailed sheep, which is already recorded by an Egyptian representation dating from the second millennium B.C. This is an Irano-Turanian animal perfectly adapted to desert or semi-desert climatic conditions. The flocks are moved to the desert when there is still quite an abundant supply of grass to be had there, and then back to the mountains, where the provision of grass is of long duration and later replaced by stubble. Towards the autumn the animals experience some privation, as they are obliged then to live for a while on their reserves.

Goats

A wild species, with long, straight horns similar to those of the ibex, exists in the Mediterranean region (Anatolia and Crete). This species used to be a native of Palestine, where its presence is vouched for in the Mesolithic era. All the present domestic species are descendants of another breed, with twisting horns, perhaps a domesticated mutational species, which is recorded in historical times. The very small breed which is reared in Palestine at the present time is obviously a strain that has adapted to desert conditions.

The donkey

Like sheep, this is not a native. It is not a descendant of the wild varieties that were once known in the Syrian desert, but of a Nubian species. It is recorded both in

Egypt and Mesopotamia right from the beginning of the historical era. In spite of its foreign origins, it has adapted itself perfectly. Breeding is carried out with a small-scale seasonal move similar to that of the sheep and goats. The donkey is the most commonly used pack animal, serving the needs of cultivator and semi-nomad alike. It is often seen in the old quarters of the towns, which are impenetrable to motor vehicles, and also on building sites where it takes the place of the wheel-barrow.

Horses

Prehistoric Palestine had a small species of the Equidae, traces of which have been found in certain neolithic sites. But the horse proper was introduced to the East only in historical times, that is at the beginning of the second millennium B.C., after it had been domesticated by the peoples coming from Persia and Armenia. It is therefore an Irano-Turanian breed, which adapted to local conditions. Breeding is easy in the steppe, but in the desert the nomadization of animals has to be very skilfully organized. In agricultural regions, fodder-growing meets with competition from cereal production, and so the horse becomes a luxury animal, reserved for the purposes of war, the use of the influential, and for postal duties on occasion. Today blood-stock breeding is falling off rapidly, and I do not know to what extent its place has been taken by race-horse breeding, in the Lebanon on the one hand, and in Israel on the other. In the villages the saddle-horses of the notabilities are not lacking in elegance, but are of fairly slender proportions. Mules have the characteristics of their parents. They are more hardy than horses and are preferred as draught animals, but are rarely used as pack-animals: for here the donkey is still the most economic of all.

The Arabian, or single-humped camel

As far as distribution is concerned, this animal is Sahara-Sindian. But in prehistoric times a wild species was known, spread in small numbers over the whole of Palestine. Probably these were destroyed or driven out at an early date as a result of hunting. The camel was not used by the first historical civilizations, but these civilizations were not completely without knowledge of the peoples who had domesticated it. For their part these peoples do not appear to have sought to establish contact. The camel was not in use on the Middle Euphrates at the beginning of the second millennium B.C. and transport was effected by means of the donkey or by man himself. Contact was restored round about the twelfth century B.C., and during the Assyrian period the camel was in normal use among the civilized populations of Mesopotamia and Syria. The development of transport during the Persian, Macedonian and Romano-Byzantine empires merely served to heighten the importance of this animal. The presence of a large beast of burden enabled the peoples of the East to do away with the need for developing roads and perfecting types of heavy vehicle. Today the camel is losing ground rapidly before the growing volume of motor transport, and breeding tends to be restricted to the camel's original habitat, where it remains the only practical form of transport.

Pigs

We know that prehistoric Palestine had several strains of wild boar. These were animals of the forest and swampland, living on acorns and roots. The pigs that were raised in a state of semi-captivity in the ancient manner, fed themselves in the same way. Independently of any kind of religious ban, pig-rearing must have fallen off at an early period as the land became increasingly deforested. The pig is very rarely to be seen nowadays, even in Christian villages.

Poultry

Hens were known from the eighth century B.C.; and at the time of the New Testament they had become common (Matt. 23. 37). Pigeons had certainly been domesticated much earlier; they were used in the rites of the Temple (Lev. 12. 6, 8), and they are still raised today. On the Arab farms one occasionally sees turkeys, but very rarely any geese and never any other type of fowl.

PART III

A HOLY LAND

by
M. DU BUIT, O.P.

CHAPTER XI

A HOLY LAND

In order to understand the place held by Palestine in the religious history of mankind, a beginning must be made with the first fact of which the Israelite mind is aware, namely that Canaan is the only place where man is able to perform a worship pleasing to God.

In Genesis we are already shown the Patriarchs erecting altars, on which they offer their sacrifices: at Sichem (Gen. 12. 6–7); at Bethel (Gen. 12. 8; 35. 1–7); at Mambre (Gen. 13. 18); at Bersabee (Gen. 21. 31–3; 26. 23–5); and at no other places. These sanctuaries, identified beyond any shadow of doubt, are situated along the central watershed of the Palestine mountains, which carries the best highway and near which lies the best land.

David chose a site in the centre of this ancient land of his fathers for his capital city, Jerusalem; and Solomon embellished the latter with a temple (2 Kings 5. 6–16; 3 Kings 5. 15 to 9. 25). The religious reforms of Josias made it the only official place of worship in Israel (4 Kings 23. 5–19), and we know that Jerusalem had been chosen in virtue of a law laid down in Deuteronomy (Deut. 12. 5–27; 14. 22–5; 15. 20; 16. 2–16. etc., cf. 4 Kings 22. 8 *seq.*).

In the other books of the Pentateuch, it is very often the worship as practised at Jerusalem that is described and regulated, through the idealized memories of the Tent of

Meeting or "Tent which bears witness to the covenant" (Knox) and the worship in the desert.

Under the influence of the Law the Israelites of the later periods, at the time of their dispersal and exile, liked to pray before an open window that faced towards Jerusalem (Dan. 6. 10; cf. Tobias 3. 11; 3 Kings 8. 48). The doors of the oldest synagogues were made to face in this direction too,[1] and under the arrangements adopted from the end of the third century A.D., the direction of Jerusalem was indicated by the cupboard containing the books of the Law, which the people faced while praying.

I have myself witnessed the deeply religious sentiments which devout Jews have for the Holy Land; they are doubly strong, because it is here that a Jew is best able to observe the laws of Moses, especially that one concerning the Sabbath day rest.

The same piety has found expression among Christians in the organizing of pilgrimages and crusades, and in the founding of numerous religious houses. We must not, however, forget the words of Jesus to the Samaritan woman: "The time is coming when you will not go to this mountain, nor yet to Jerusalem to worship the Father. . . . The time is coming, nay, has already come, when true worshippers will worship the Father in spirit and in truth" (John 4. 21–3). Our piety towards the Holy Land must be freed from all traces of legalism, but the Bible itself invites us to understand how Palestine was suited in many ways to the meeting of God and man.

The country was, and remains, a witness to the many events of sacred history. It was a good land, one that lent itself to the growth of communities and to men's development.

The great idolatrous cultures of antiquity met in strife on this ground.

[1] See *Biblical Archeology*, Volume 62 in this series, page 54.

The proximity of the desert favoured the vocations of the prophets.

A WITNESS TO SACRED HISTORY

The first thing that surprises the pilgrim to the Holy Land is the large number of perfectly identified ancient sites. All the place-names of any importance in the Old Testament—more than half the total—and almost all those in the New Testament, are known today with adequate or even absolute certainty.

The reason for this is that even as early as antiquity, sacred writers were careful to pinpoint the various places in the Land of Israel that were the scene of the main events in sacred history. Very often we find in their books such indications as this: "(Josue) set up twelve stones, which are there to this day" (Josue 4. 9; cf. 7. 26; 8. 28–9; 10. 27, etc.). The continual preservation of Jewish and Christian communities and the unbroken practice of making pilgrimages have kept tradition alive. Again and again devout investigators have been able to get back to the sources and to reliable evidence. They have enabled us, even today, to enjoy the greater part of the work of the sacred writers.

Learned research on Palestine can be grouped into three periods.

The talmudist rabbis (between the first and fourth centuries A.D.) have fixed in their accounts the location for numerous biblical place-names, especially in Galilee, which was the centre of Jewish life at that time.

Among the Fathers of the Church during the fourth and fifth centuries, Eusebius, the bishop of Caesarea in Palestine and author of the valuable *Ecclesiastical History*, compiled a veritable dictionary of biblical place-names, establishing their present name and location. This work was translated into Latin by St Jerome, who added several other indications to it in his *Commentaries*.

In the nineteenth and twentieth centuries, many explorers travelled on horseback throughout Palestine: they visited each village and each set of ruins, and found once more on the spot the indications given by the Bible and by the ancient scholars. Among their number, we may quote the names of the Americans Robinson and Albright, the Englishmen Conder and Warren, the Germans Dalman and Alt, and the Frenchmen Clermont-Ganneau and Abel, to mention only the chief ones. Although we can never rule out the possibility of surprise discoveries, this work may be said to be completed now, and the trend today is towards detailed investigation of the most interesting sites

This represents a great work accomplished over the course of the centuries in order to preserve the topographical traditions of Palestine. For there was a vital need for it in the Jewish and Christian religions: they are both historical religions founded as a result of events that are situated in time and space. They normally awaken in all believers the desire to see the actual places, and in the most enlightened of their responsible members the desire to verify and ensure the "certainty concerning the teaching which has been received" (cf. Luke 1. 4).

Certainly, from the critical point of view, the identification of the sites is not enough to guarantee the historical authenticity of a story completely, though this is a serious argument in its favour. The problem of the literary style cannot be solved by this reason alone, and there are fictitious accounts closely linked with a particular province or town. But taking the matter strictly at its minimum value, the local origin is very well backed up, and in the Bible we are always dealing with the book of a real country and of a real people.

It is impossible here to go into the wealth of detail concerning the topography of the Bible. This has been done in several excellent works, and the reader will have no difficulty in finding in them all the information that he may require. A study of these books, indispensable to anyone wishing to undertake the journey to the Holy Land, is calculated to "foster a joyful increase in faith" in all, as St Paul says (cf. Phil. 1. 25), or rather to surround it with those visible signs which enable it to evoke the whole personality of a man.

A GOOD LAND

While it is easy to recognize many traces of the past in Palestine, it is much less easy to understand how the Bible could possibly have described it as "a land that is all milk and honey" (Exod. 3. 8, etc.).

On the contrary, any traveller who approaches the country from the Arab zone is struck by its primitiveness and poverty, while anybody travelling in Israel is inclined to admire the great technical achievements of the Zionists, rather than the country's resources.

Moreover, the Christian pilgrim is rather inclined to consider the Holy Land as a poor country, following the example of men such as Charles de Foucauld and Paul Gauthier, an attitude that could, indeed, quickly become an unhealthy one, if it were not closely linked with a genuine involvement in the way of life recommended in the Gospels.

In any case, the inhabitants of Palestine have quite a different feeling towards their country, and triumphant Jews and fugitive Arabs would for once be in agreement in subscribing to these words taken from Deuteronomy:

"The Lord thy God means to settle thee in a fair land, a land that has water coursing down in streams, and deep wells that break out from plain and hill; a land of wheat and barley, of vine and fig-tree and pomegranate, and olive, a land where oil flows and honey. Here without fear of want thou mayest win thy livelihood; all shall be thine in abundance . . . here thou mayest eat thy fill and bless the name of the Lord thy God for the fair land he has given thee" (Deut. 8. 7–10).

In order to understand such words, which are by no means unique in the Bible, the modern traveller has first to undergo a double remove from what he is used to: he has to undergo a remove in space and in time.

Firstly, he must not compare Palestine to our provinces that have a maritime climate, but rather to the Mediterranean countries of Europe, from Spain to Greece. In such a setting, Palestine holds a respectable position, for roughly everywhere one finds cultivation in the same stages.

First there is a coastal plain, which in its natural state is unhealthy, but which, after draining and irrigation, bears rich fruit, market-garden and industrial crops. In addition to the citrus plantations, there are, in Palestine, banana and palm plantations. This plain is the only part of the country that lends itself to modern methods: large-scale public works, provision of fertilizers, utilization of machines, and consequently the cultivation of crops that are rich, but also heavy in their requirements. And so here a general expansion in agriculture can be achieved today, and it is the same with industry, which is closely dependent on transport facilities.

The hills of medium or low altitude are usually dry and rocky. They have small fields laid out on terraces, and small plantations of vines, olive-trees or other fruit-trees; this zone, with its often steep slopes, is not suited to the use of machines. Only the valleys and small plateaus further towards the interior, where there has been a deposit of good red soil, are able to provide good yields, but the area of such spots is very small. In the western Mediterranean, in Haute Provence or Corsica for example, this tier was still well populated a hundred years ago, but it would become completely uninhabited now but for the tourist industry, which is responsible for some activity there today.

One tier alone is missing in Palestine, namely that of hills of medium height, reserved for pine and evergreen-oak forests; it is only represented here by a few 2600-ft hills in Galilee, Transjordan, Judaea and on Mount Carmel. It must be realized that in Palestine the forests have been destroyed even more than in Europe, and that what forest there is to be seen today in Israel represents the fruits borne by a great reafforestation scheme. It must also be stated that the Mediterranean-type forests, which produce little useful timber, have never been of any great economic value in meeting the ordinary requirements of the local inhabitants; and this explains why the latter were so little interested in conserving the forests. To say today that the ancient peoples of this land were wrong to clear the forest from the hills as much as possible, is to show ignorance of the times.

If we go back into the past, we must first of all remember that the Mediterranean climatic zone was, during the whole of antiquity and up to the end of the sixteenth century A.D., a region in which human activity was very intense, on economic and cultural levels alike. In Roman times, the entire Orient was a region of great activity, densely populated and crossed by many roads. As for Palestine, the towns here formed a network in which the links were the stretches of roads between them, 15 to 30 miles in length, on the same pattern as in western Europe. Seven centuries earlier, during the kingdoms of Israel and Judah, the lists given in Josue, which have since been corroborated by archeological exploration, indicate even at that early date a heavily populated country, in which human settlements reach far out into the desert areas. We are told in

2 Paralipomena: "Towers, too, [King Ozias] built out in the desert, and dug cisterns in plenty, for his many herds that grazed both in the lowlands and in the desert solitudes; he had vines, too, and vine-dressers to tend them in the hill country and about the town of Carmel" (2 Paral. 26. 10).

The Palestine of Isaias and Jeremias, of Jesus and his disciples, was a rich and thriving country, in which the more serious political altercations had not yet sapped the natural vigour of her men. The combined weight of textual and archeological evidence on this point obliges us to reverse completely our first impressions. To us the Mediterranean zone is generally a poor one, containing occasional enclaves of prosperity: this was not the case in antiquity.

In order to see the reason for this, we must first realize the wide range of agricultural produce yielded by the soil: wheat—"the staff of life" (cf. Lev. 26. 26; Ps. 105. 16; Ezech. 4. 16; 5. 16; 14. 13), wine "in which both God and man delight" (Judges 9. 13), lentils, which appease the ravenous hunger of the hunter (Gen. 25. 29–34), the various kinds of fruit; and in particular olive oil, which was used as food, medicine and perfume: Solomon used it to pay King Hiram of Tyre (3 Kings 5. 11), and the Psalmist liked to pour "it on the head till it flows down on to the beard" (Ps. 132. 2), also the Good Samaritan used it to treat the wounds of the injured traveller (Luke 10. 34).

These foods, together with milk and milk-products and a small amount of meat, still provide the peoples of the Levant with a healthy, balanced diet. Although poverty has left visible marks on them, it is not so serious as to have brought about a lowering in their physical condition. Travellers accustomed to journeying all over the East are struck by the healthy appearance of the inhabitants of the Mediterranean seaboard, and by their capacity for progress.

Also, it must be remembered that the crops are distributed fairly evenly over the land. There are very few

villages where it is impossible to grow most of the crops
mentioned above; and there are few families in which a
man cannot expect to eat the produce of his own threshing-
floor, and to enjoy the wine from his own grapes and the
milk from his own cows and take his rest in the shade
of his own fig-tree (3 Kings 4. 25; 4 Kings 18. 31; Ps. 4. 8;
Mich. 4. 4; Zach. 3. 10).

Moreover, the tending of the vine and of trees calls
for more skill than the very simple work of tilling the soil;
it also requires the cultivator to be fixed to the land and
to have a long-term interest in its production (cf. the
parable of the vine-dressers, Matt. 21. 33–4). Sociologists
who have made a study of the traditional East between
the two world wars have observed that peasants engaged
in orcharding in the coastal areas had at that time a better
social status than those engaged in cereal farming on the
steppe towards the interior of Syria. Among the former,
private property or at least family holdings were the rule,
and there was some personal initiative. Among the cereal
farmers, however, ownership was on a collective, communal basis with the village as the unit, and this made it
easy for a wealthy landowner or money-lender to lay his
hands on the communal possessions and to transform the
peasant into a kind of serf.

In biblical times it is likely, and in keeping, moreover,
with the spirit of the sacred books, that the family was not
swallowed up in the village, nor the village in the kingdom. The age-old cry of independence, "To your tents,
Israel" (3 Kings 12. 16), was always ready to ring out in
the ears of the mighty, and made them behave to some
extent circumspectly. The fact that the books of the
prophets are filled with imprecations against the injustices
of the powerful and the rich goes to show that there were
men who were free enough to understand these calls and
remember them.

The land of Israel was indeed a good land: not vast like
Syria or Mesopotamia, where the open plains were suited
to every kind of undertaking; and not extremely fertile
like Egypt or Babylon, where wealth and power piled up
of their own accord in huge capital cities, ready to be used
in the expansion of those great idolatrous civilizations.
But it was a land where life was pleasant and where the
human personality found a happy, balanced environment
in which to develop, in close proximity to God the Creator.
A passage in Deuteronomy fittingly expresses this quality
possessed by the Holy Land:

> The land which lies before you . . . is a country of hill and
> dale, that waits for rain from heaven to water it, so that the
> Lord your God himself must be at pains to tend it, watching
> over it from year's end to year's end. And if you obey the
> commands I am giving you now, by loving the Lord and
> serving him, heart and soul, then he will send your land
> rain in autumn, rain in spring, to give you a harvest of
> wheat, and wine and oil; your beasts will have grass to graze
> on in the countryside, and you food to your hearts' content
> (Deut. 11. 10–15).

The traveller in the Holy Land must make himself
keenly aware of these fundamental natural circumstances
by observing carefully all the traces of man's work and
habitation.[1]

THE CLASH OF CIVILIZATIONS

Palestine may have been a good land in biblical times,
but it was not easy to enjoy it in peace. As today, it lay
at the crossroads between Egypt and Mesopotamia; and the
route between these two great political centres served as a
highway both for trade and for war. As today, Palestine
lay open to intrusion from the direction of the sea. To

---

[1] Such observation is easier if Palestine is approached after first
passing through Syria and crossing tracts of arid land and desert.

anyone who is interested in current events, this is obvious;
in antiquity, however, it was a question of much more:
each empire was both a culture and an idolatrous religion.
There is no better way of having this fact brought home,
than by visiting the rooms of Egyptian and oriental
antiquities at the British Museum and, at the same time,
consulting the guide-book; this is an excellent preliminary
exercise before undertaking biblical studies or a visit to
the Holy Land.

Of course, there were several periods in this history of
Israel when true independence was achieved, the finest
among them being the reigns of David and Solomon. But
taken as a whole, this history can be plotted out as a continual struggle for survival in the face of various idolatrous
systems. It was a triumphant struggle against the commercial predominance of Tyre, which was associated with the
cult of Baal (from 885 to 841 B.C., 3 Kings 16. 23. to 4
Kings 10. 27). It was an unfortunate struggle by the kingdom of Israel against Assyrian imperialism (from 805 to
721 B.C.). It was a longer struggle by the kingdom of Judah
caught between the attacks of Assur, and later of Babylon,
and the Egyptian counter-attacks (from 736 to 587 B.C.).
But here, the encroachment was also a spiritual one: the
conquered kings, Achaz and later on Manasses, had
adopted the Assyrian worship of the heavenly bodies, the
"host of heaven" (4 Kings 16. 10–18, and 21. 5). On the
other hand, Ezechias was a convinced monotheist, who
rebelled as much against the religious as against the military domination. For Josias, restoration of national liberty
was the means to a religious reformation.

Ultimately, national purpose grew weak, Jerusalem was
captured and her people carried off to Babylon (587), but
religious strength continued, centred around the figures of
Jeremias and Ezechiel, and "a remnant" remained faithful
to the one God (cf. Isaias 6. 13, etc). And this small

nucleus was to re-establish the holy nation under the more liberal empire of the Persians, from 538 B.C. onwards.

When a new idolatrous culture made its appearance in the East, in Greece, the faith of Israel was able to resist its influence. The struggle was extremely fierce at two points: the first of these culminated in the victory of the Machabees over the Greeks of Syria (167–139 B.C.); the second ended in defeat at the hands of the Romans, among whom the cult of the Emperor assumed increasing importance (68–70 A.D.). The preaching of the Gospel took place at a moment of relative calm between the two storms, and was to transform the old religion of Israel in such a way that thenceforth it could take root and spread in all lands.

Time after time Israel was delivered from her enemies; in the end she seems to have realized that true freedom is not a basic fact of nature, but rather a gift from God—a gift that is always fragile, that must be earned, awaited and requested. The ancient memory of the Pasch, of deliverance, that is, from Egyptian bondage, was constantly cherished and revived by the more recent occasions for hope and liberation. The God of goodness and might made himself known as the one who frees and wishes men to be free, as in most religions of antiquity; the Law laid down: "And if thy brother Israelite is brought by poverty to sell his own liberty to thee, do not submit him to bondage with thy slaves. ... The Israelites know no master but me, their rescuer from Egypt" (Lev. 25. 39–42). It seems reasonable to suppose that the situation of Palestine on the fringes of the great civilizations of ancient times encouraged the development of such preoccupations in the religious conscience.

Today, this land is a witness once more to the clash of nations and cultures. It is now the bone of contention between Jew and Moslem, both of whom are more or less obsessed by the spirit of modern civilization, which is out of keeping with their ancestral traditions. Christians are represented here by a solid local minority (approximately 10 per cent in Jordan, and between 6 and 7 per cent in Israel), reinforced by numerous foreign residents.

At present attention remains focused on the political problems, but in the background there remain, as in the past, religious problems. The pilgrim in the Holy Land has not the means at his disposal for a thorough study of them, but at least he should take them into serious consideration and remain keenly aware of them. He should approach the opposing religions with respectful interest, visit their principal sanctuaries, and acquaint himself with the undertakings for the reclamation of the land. In all this, he must feel the presence around him of men who are creatures of flesh and blood. Perhaps a solution will one day emerge from this dispute that can now be observed.

THE DESERT: THE TRAINING-GROUND OF THE PROPHETS

Having been herself forced to bow many times in the past to foreign influences, Palestine has seen how each such influence has been wiped out by its successor. Neighbouring Phoenicia, on the contrary, assimilated all of them. A visit to a museum, for example the British Museum, reveals this fact at the first glance: the cases of exhibits from Palestine are very poor in figures, whether human or other, and excavations that have been made on the spot show a gap. But Phoenicia has yielded up a great number of figures, in which can be seen Egyptian or Mesopotamian influence, and also Greek at a later stage. This syncretism in images points to syncretism in the mythologies that are closely associated with them. Thus, we see that in two countries that were alike in so many ways, men reacted differently. Can such a difference be explained in part by the qualities of the Holy Land?

The Bible itself appears to invite us to think so, when it relates that several of the great inspired leaders of Israel stayed for long periods in the desert: Moses (Exod. 2. 15 to 4. 17); Elias (3 Kings 17. 2–6 and 19); then John the Baptist (Luke 1. 80 and 3. 2); Jesus (Matt. 4. 1–11); and finally Paul of Tarsus (Gal. 1. 17). And when the Bible tells at great length in Exodus and Numbers about Israel's sojourn in the wilderness, it is very likely that it enriches an historical memory with the spiritual experience of several generations of "sons of prophets", such as the disciples of Elias and Eliseus who joined forces in the Jordan desert (4 Kings 2. 4–8; 6. 1–7). At an early date Christian monks set their hearts on renewing this tradition.

Not that the desert gave rise, as it has been asserted sometimes, to monotheism. Everything that is known about the ancient tribes of the Syrian desert, and also about the Arabs before the coming of Islam, shows them to have been polytheistic. The Bible also informs us that the ancestors of the Patriarchs "served alien gods" (Gen. 31. 13–35; 35. 2–4). But it is true that living in the desert toughens a man's body, at the same time simplifying and concentrating his thoughts, and so the desert was conducive to a deepening of faith in one God.

The Palestine wilderness provides a symbolism which in turn helps to create and foster certain dispositions of the soul. Its proximity to the habitable parts was able to provide subjects for meditation. From the top of the Mount of Olives, as today, could be seen Jerusalem and her gardens in one direction, and in the other the desert with its buff-coloured hills and red-hued walls or rock. How better to illustrate the belief that all the possessions of the earth are the gift of God, and that he distributes them according to his will, causing the rain "that fell on one city, and not on the next" (Amos 4. 7).

To go deep into the wilderness could mean for a prophet

of old to depart from the idolatrous sanctuaries set up by the Canaanites "on every hill and under every green tree" (Deut. 12. 2; 3 Kings 14. 23, etc.; Jer. 2. 20, etc.); Israel had never lost the habit of frequenting them. Christian monks later on were to flee not from idolatry, but from riches and a civilization that was too highly developed.

As the solitary went further, he would find the terrain becoming increasingly arid, cut by deep ravines and frightening precipices. But he also found spacious views, devoid of any monotony, with the Dead Sea shining a deep blue in the background. In winter, the rain-washed air imparted a sharpness to the contours of the mountains, and gave brightness to their colours, adding a charm and poetic quality. The temperature, really cold elsewhere, would become mild, and it was not difficult to find the shelter of a cave. The rain would fall and grass shoots appear, and a few flocks would wander over the slopes, their shepherds skilled, as they still are, in gathering edible plants, which also served well the needs of prophets and monks (cf. 4 Kings 4. 39). But the summer would soon return, and with it the drought.

In the absolute silence, scarcely disturbed by the call of an animal, man heard only the sound of his own voice, echoing either the Adversary of mankind—the whole of monastic tradition bears witness to the fact—or else to the Creator.

Can we discern some remembrance of life in the wilderness and its contrasts in the following dialogue of Jeremias with his God:

> Lord, bethink thee, and come to my defence. When thy words were found, how greedily I devoured them! Great joy and content those words gave my heart. . . . Why are those sad thoughts still with me? Is my heart desperate, beyond all remedy? Did it cheat me, like some empty water course, my hope in thee? (Jer. 15. 15–20).

Certainly the desert did not make the prophet, but it attracted him and helped him to grow strong in his vocation. In the words of Osee, it was there that God "speaks to the heart".

The need for the desert is so real that artificial ones, in our monasteries, have been created in Christian lands. And in them we see the same material severity, the same sober beauty, attractive and frightening at the same time, the same moral simplicity, the same silence and solitude before God. To a certain extent, the Mohammedan dervishes fulfil a similar rôle. In the case of Israel, her entire exile can be thought of in terms of a sojourn in the "desert of the peoples" (and in a foreign world, deaf and silent, where the ghettoes were only camps or, at the most, oases). As it came to maturity in the desert, the religion of Moses and the prophets, and also of Jesus, to all intents and purposes carries the desert about with it.

In Palestine, even today, the desert is never far away. Even in those regions enjoying the highest fertility, it takes only a rocky hill or a bare dune to remind one for an instant of its appearance; and it is only necessary to travel for about 15 or 20 miles in order to come to it. The Israelis' great enthusiasm for the agricultural development of the Negev desert in the south does not come from purely economic motives, but far more from a desire to make up for the helplessness suffered over a long past. Can it be that among some of these pioneers there is a presentiment of something else? For them, as indeed for all men, the way to spiritual adventure lies open.

A land where sacred history remains a living reality, a good land of free men, swept by all the great storms of human history, a land where the hermit's dwelling adjoins the town—such was the Holy Land in the past, and such it still is, or can be, today. It is no longer the privileged

centre for God's worship and obedience to the laws of
Moses, yet it remains as a living, abiding lesson in religious
wisdom, and perhaps it is destined to become once more
the land where the Spirit of God speaks for all men.

CHAPTER XII

SUGGESTIONS FOR A
PILGRIMAGE

Most pilgrims seek and find in the Holy Land a certain ease in prayer, and what might be called a quickening of faith. By this is meant the spiritual satisfaction derived from seeing and touching the relics of those events around which their faith centres, and in which they acknowledge the gifts that God has made to men.

Nothing is more normal in a historical religion, founded upon actual events, one in which each event has its date and place. However, it must be realized that excess is possible here, and that this has already happened on more than one occasion. Many of the so-called "houses", "prisons", "caves" and "rocks" that are held up for the veneration of travellers are nothing else than the natural response to their naïve and pious greed. Even learned clerics have not always escaped this.

The most enlightened pilgrim will, it is hoped, go and pray with those who were in the past, and who still are today, his brothers. Let him remember that many sanctuaries have been kept up over the past centuries only at the cost of courageous and sustained efforts, but let him not become inordinately attached to the detail of what is shown to him.

He should devote all his attention to the country as a whole, for it can be taken for granted that, except for rare exceptions, the places he visits really are the places mentioned in the Bible, and that the countryside he sees is indeed the one which Christ, the prophets and the Apostles saw. As some humorist has put it, "in the churches of the Holy Land you pray with your eyes shut, and then you go outside and look".

What should the pilgrim see? As much as possible, bringing his whole personality and culture to bear, and not only when he visits the famous places, but also as he travels along the roads. Chiefly he must be entirely imbued with the idea that he is in a real country and not some place specially arranged for visitors. And so he will observe all the activities of the everyday life and work of the inhabitants, in the fields and the workshops. But he must go about it in a discreet manner, for nobody likes to be subjected to the curious gaze of strangers; in short, he must be alert and as far as possible informed, and reading this little book may be a help in this direction.

In order to arrive at an understanding, the traveller should be careful not to compare a foreign country too readily with his own. And therefore it is a good thing to begin a pilgrimage by as thorough a separation as possible from one's normal environment. There is no better way of producing this effect than by journeying overland from Beirut to Jerusalem. To cross the two mountain passes separating the Lebanon from Syria, to undergo the experience of leaving the Mediterranean and entering the continent of Asia, to make a brief visit to Damascus, an ancient Aramaean city and today one of the capitals of the Arab world, to cross the Syrian steppes and the desert at the Jordan frontier, to see the stunted oaks appearing one by one—a sign of return to a more humid climate—

all these are experiences which the traveller by air misses, and in doing so misses certain aspects of the Bible.

If a longer journey is desired the experience may be partially replaced by a visit to Petra, the ancient capital of the Nabataeans. This route will also take us over a great expanse of steppes and deserts before we reach the legendary land of Arabia, and see the unusual shapes and colours of the granite and lava formations of the extreme south.

After an experience of this nature, we can more easily see that the Mediterranean mountain region of Palestine is still a good land, and that it was perhaps more so at one time. During the time spent in this region—and it will be the major portion of the visit—we should try to observe the farm crops and the plantations. In the Arab part of the land, which has remained more traditional, one will easily recognize many vestiges of the way of life of the biblical farmers.

At the same time as breaking away from our customary surroundings, we must also break away from the present and take ourselves back in time to the great civilizations of the ancient East. And here there is perhaps no better way of preparing for a visit to the Holy Land than by making a careful study of the Egyptian and oriental antiquities at the British Museum or the Louvre. Two afternoons is not too much to prepare oneself adequately for a visit to the Holy Land of more than a fortnight. One should begin with the Egyptian exhibits, which are less varied than the others, and visit the various rooms in turn, using the guide-book. Particular attention should be given to the dates, and these should be compared afterwards with the dates given in a good chronological table of the Bible; and it will be seen that the Egyptian civilization had already reached its zenith by the time Moses led the tribes of Israel out of Egypt.

Afterwards, one should pay a visit to the Oriental antiquities. Here we see traces of the more diverse and more complex civilizations which fought one another and succeeded one another until the spread of Hellenism. Here, too, particular attention should be paid to the dates, comparing them with those of events in the Bible. We should also try to feel the spiritual force attached to certain figures, for example the Sumerian statues of worshippers, or the stele of Hammurabi, representing a dialogue between man and the Deity. The visitor will see here a power of concentration which is ordinarily absent from the Egyptian exhibits, and which the Bible transmits to us in literary form today. He will see once more that this book was written after the greatest period of Oriental civilization, and that it contains all that is best of the latter and in what might be described as a concentrated and purified form.

In the East itself, there are several museums housing beautiful and fascinating exhibits. The one which is the easiest to visit, and the most instructive, is the Rockefeller Museum in Jerusalem, in the Jordanian sector of the city. Even pilgrims who do not care for these studies would be wrong to miss the chance of a visit. For this museum provides a very useful means of fitting Bible history into the general context of history as a whole.

The pilgrim will emerge from all these experiences with a conviction that the Bible is the book of a real people, who lived in the presence of God; and it is for this reason that it continues to speak to us so eloquently about God.

But there are other representatives of this chosen people: these are the men living in the Holy Land today. First the Israelis, who speak the language of that people and adhere more or less strictly to their law and traditions, are fully justified in claiming descent from them. On the other hand, it must not be forgotten that the Arabs of the Levant are also connected with the people of the Bible in many aspects of their customs and way of life. The simple, sincere piety of the Moslems, especially perhaps of those in humbler walks of life, their way of referring constantly to God, whose presence they feel, their customary dignity, their family spirit and patience—all of this preserves a large part of the authentic biblical heritage.

It is indeed true that the pilgrim is unable to enter into close contact with the various races among whom he will move in the course of his travels, but it is to be hoped that he will feel deeply the surprising and profound difference between them and the rest of humanity, with whom he is used to coming into contact; and also that his experience will remain with him as an unanswered and perhaps unanswerable question.

Of course, there is need at all times, to observe perfect courtesy and also to show a certain reserve. It should be remembered that these are foreign countries which have not much reason for friendliness. The numerous traces left over from the Crusades and colonization are perhaps not a subject for unalloyed pride, and a visit to the memorial to the Jewish martyrs and to the tomb of David leaves the traveller with a painful, but perhaps salutary memory.

Even the Christian sanctuaries produce an unfortunate impression sometimes, on account of the divisions and quarrels between the rival bodies of clergy. The whole of Christian life in the East bears the sorry stamp of the attempts of one group to rob another of its churches and followers. The progress made over the past few years has not yet succeeded in healing the age-old wounds. We must experience this unfortunate aspect of Church history, and rejoice at the same time at walking in the footsteps of the saintly people who have kept alive the memory and imitation of Jesus Christ in the very land where he lived among men.

SELECT BIBLIOGRAPHY

In this series: Du Buit, François, O.P.; *Biblical Archeology.*

Albright, W. F.: *The Archeology of Palestine,* Harmondsworth and Baltimore, Penguin Books, 1956; *The Archeology and Religion of Israel,* Baltimore, Johns Hopkins Press, 1941.

Baly, Denis: *Geography of the Bible,* New York, Harper, 1957.

Bentwich, N.: *Israel and her Neighbours,* London, Rider, 1960; *The Jews in Our Time,* London and Harmondsworth, Penguin Books, 1960.

Dearden, A.: *Jordan,* London, Hale, 1958; *Economic Development of Jordan,* Baltimore, Johns Hopkins Press, 1957.

Fisher, W. B.: *The Middle East,* London, Methuen, 1950.

Grollenberg, L. H., O.P.: *Atlas of the Bible,* translated and edited by H. H. Rowley and J. M. H. Reid, London and New York, Nelson, 1956.

Harris, G. L.: *Jordan,* New York, Taplinger, 1958.

Konikoff, A.: *Transjordan, an Economic Survey,* Jerusalem, Economic Research Institute, 1946.

Orni, E., and Efrat, E.: *Geography of Israel,* Jerusalem, Israel Program for Scientific Translations, 1964.

Pritchard, J. B.: *The Ancient Near East in Pictures Relating to the Old Testament,* Princeton, N.J., Princeton Univ. Press, 1955.

Rowe, Alan: *The Topography and History of Beth-Shan,* Philadelphia, Pa, Philadelphia Univ. Press, 1930.

Tavener, L. E.: *The Revival of Israel,* London, Hodder and Stoughton, 1961.